the cosmic clocks

BY THE SAME AUTHOR:

The Influence of the Stars: A Critical and Experimental Study (L'Influence des Astres, Étude Critique et Expérimentale). Paris: Dauphin, 1955.

Men and Stars (Les Hommes et les Astres). Paris: Denoël, 1960.

Astrology Facing Science (L'Astrologie Devant la Science). Paris: Planète, 1965.

Planetary Heredity (L'Hérédité Planétaire). Paris: Planète, 1966.

Atmospheric Conditions and Health (La Santé et les Conditions Atmosphériques). Paris: Hachette, 1967.

In collaboration with Françoise Gauquelin:

Methods for the Study of the Partitioning of Stars in the Diurnal Movement (Méthodes pour Étudier la Répartition des Astres dans le Mouvement Diurne). Paris, 1957.

Psychology in the Twentieth Century (La Psychologie an XXᵉ Siècle). Paris: Editions Sociales Françaises, 1963.

the cosmic clocks

from astrology to a modern science

michel gauquelin

Foreword by Frank A. Brown, Jr.

Permission has been granted by the publishers to use quo-
tations from the following works: Louis MacNeice, *Astrology* (Doubleday & Company, Inc.); Franz Cumont, *Astrology
and Religion Among the Greeks and Romans* (Dover Pub-
lications, Inc.); R. Tocquet, *Cycles et Rythmes* (Dunod
Éditeur); Arthur Koestler, *The Sleepwalkers* (The Macmillan Company); Darrell Huff, *Cycles in Your Life* (W. W.
Norton & Co., Inc.); Rachel Carson, *The Sea Around Us*
(Oxford University Press); G. Piccardi, "Exposé Introductif" in *Symposium Internationale sur les Relations Phe-
nomenales Solaire et Terrestriale* (Presses Académiques
Européennes); G. Piccardi, *The Chemical Basis of Medical
Climatology* (Charles C. Thomas, Publisher); E. Hunting-
ton, *Season of Birth* (John Wiley & Sons, Inc.).

Foreword

THE STORY that Michel Gauquelin recounts in a fascinating and stimulating manner relates to the long history of man's imaginative and scientific excursions as he observed and contemplated on his relations to the heavens. The story covers from the earliest astrological speculations, even far antedating the modern science of astronomy, to the present. It is a vivid, exciting account of the evolution of human thought on the subject from the time the heavens were viewed simply with awe, wonder, and reverence to the present space-oriented age, when our explosively expanding knowledge has proven that living creatures are tied to their Universe in subtle ways unimagined a few short years ago.

Man, from the earliest dawning of his mind in the remote past, has doubtless struggled to understand his position in the hierarchy of nature. He has strived continuously to learn his relationships to the Universe about him, a Universe over which he felt he had little or no control, and which he felt, intuitively, exerted an inexorable control over him. The most inaccessible and seemingly inevitable of these were the movements of sun, moon, and other celestial bodies. Their dependable presence and movements he could relate to the day and night, the ocean tides, and the seasons.

In searching for security and understanding it was only natural that man turned to the seemingly all-powerful, permanent, and dependable heavens. But lacking a means of really knowing anything he invented relations that served to provide him with confidence, whether justifiably or not. For man, there exists a deep-seated need for beliefs. How many among us remain completely unmindful of one or another of the innumerable popular superstitions or do not secretly entertain lucky numbers or good-luck charms of one kind or other?

For modern civilized man "science" has largely replaced superstitions. He looks importantly to "science" for the solutions of all his problems as he once looked to the heavens and his gods. But "science" based upon rationalized "truths" derived from increasingly accurate observations of nature and often retestable by obtaining predictable results from controlled, experimentally manipulated conditions is not entirely unlike the superstitions it replaces, in that its "truths" are uncertain "shifting sands." The "truths" of one generation may become absurdities of a succeeding one. Our treatises in science demand steady revisions, not simply to add the new "truths," but almost equally to shed that which has meanwhile ceased to be "true." The history of mankind has been a steady, continuous groping toward understanding the actual "nature of things." At every step of the way there have occurred some "truths" more durable and some less so.

Mankind made tremendous progress in things now deemed in the domain of science long before the advent of modern science. To name but a few, there are the domestication of animals and plants, the prediction of celestial events, and the discovery and useful application of natural pharmacological agents, as, for example, curare. Science, defined as a knowledge of man's internal and external environments and his employment of it for his own welfare, is undoubtedly as ancient as man himself.

Since even the "truths" of modern science may become very different over the brief span of a few years, it is to be expected that over hundreds or thousands of years of history they would undergo far more tremendous changes. Small wonder man continues to grope beyond his current science, even as scientists steadily do themselves, both as human beings and as scientists.

Although man has long speculated that the heavens in some mysterious manner controlled his being and activities, this seemed impossible to the modern scientist who constantly sought out the means by which causes and effects were mediated. In the absence of any obvious means, the existence of any direct relationships whatsoever between living creatures and the heavens was held in the gravest of doubt, doubt that was reinforced through the finding that one after another of the claimed relationships of the astrologers would not withstand critical evaluation.

Biologists became increasingly deeply occupied in the study of the biological roles of the obvious factors of the environment, ones that they could readily alter experimentally and whose actions could be easily resolved. These included light, temperature, and mechanical and chemical factors. Science moved forward so rapidly and successfully that there was firm conviction on the part of nearly everyone that all could and would ultimately be accountable in terms of the interactions of living creatures with these well-recognized, obvious factors. Definite hostility met anyone who as much as suggested the possibility that one might search for subtle celestial influences. Such an area was off-limits for the research activities of any respectable biologist.

In the early 1950's, two new areas of research began to

attract the attention of scholars. These were the phenomena of biological clocks and compasses.

A wide gamut of kinds of animals and plants were
found to be able to "know" the periods of the days, the
tides, the months, and even the years, even while being
deprived of every obvious cue that should presumably
have enabled them to do so. In keeping with the widespread conviction that all was accountable in terms of
the organism's interacting with its "obvious-factor" environment, it was rationalized that since none of these
latter factors gave the organism the timing information,
each organism must contain the required independent
timing system within itself. To contemplate the alternative—that the organisms received some occult timing
information—was tantamount to opening a "Pandora's
Box" and loosing upon biology insurmountable problems on top of already discouragingly complex ones.

The existence of some uncannily precise timing capacity of life became underscored as investigators of the
homing and navigational capacities of birds, fishes, insects, and crustaceans learned that all these creatures appeared to practice celestial navigation. The sun could be
used as a compass, or the moon, or the constellations.
But, of course, geographic orientation by means of celestial references demanded that the animal "know" the
position in the sky that these heavenly references would
be located at any given instant. The animals' "internal
timers" were invoked to surmount this difficulty. Needed
were "clocks" that timed the earth's rotation relative to
the sun (24 hours), the moon (24 hours, 50 minutes),
and the stars (23 hours, 56 minutes). A veritable cal-
endar-clock system was clearly demanded.

But meanwhile investigations of the biological clocks
were disclosing that the "clocks" were themselves prob-

ably timed by subtle, pervasive variations in the earth's atmosphere effected by the relative movements of the earth, sun, and moon. Many demonstrable characters of the "clocks" could be rationally accounted for only in terms of the organism's steadily receiving timing information from its physical environment. It was becoming more and more apparent that the celestial bodies were somehow simultaneously involved in the "compasses" of animals and the "clocks" upon which these compasses had appeared to depend. The means by which the living creatures oriented their activities in time and in space seemed to be merging into one.

By what means was such information on time and space conveyed to the presumably shielded organisms? By an extensive and intensive study, during the past several years, of the systematically changing right- or left-turning tendencies of populations of animals with time and geographic direction for a variety of animal species, it was learned 1) that in an unchanging field of artificial illumination the animals' orientational tendencies vary systematically with all the natural periods related to the relative movements of the earth, sun, and moon, and 2) that at any given moment in time, the orientational tendency varies systematically with the geographic directional relationship of that field of illumination. Again, the factors involved in orientation in time and space appeared to merge into one.

A search for the pervasive atmospheric factors in this phenomenon revealed a fantastic responsiveness of living things to the very weak magnetic, electrostatic, and electromagnetic fields of the earth. Responses could be simulated as responses to correspondingly weak, artificial experimental fields. Whatever the means at the disposal of the living system, it could distinguish among directions and strengths of these very weak fields. That these were in some manner specialized sensitivities was evident in that the maximum resolving capacity of the animals for the artificially produced fields lay at the very same weak levels as the earth's natural fields. It has even proven possible to deceive organisms—to have them respond to spurious "times and directions" just as they do to the natural conditions—by appropriate laboratory manipulations of the very weak electromagnetic fields.

In hundreds of millions of years of evolution on this planet life has apparently become beautifully adapted to the earth's subtle, pervasive geophysical fields, as well as to the more familiar obvious ones.

Experimental evidence is rapidly amassing that living creatures can "feel" time, expressed in terms of physical events locked to angular coordinates in the natural cycles of their cosmic environment—dispensing with the need of critical measurements of these time intervals by self-contained means within their individual bodies—and that each individual regulates its own activities accordingly and in its own way. For example, the annual variation observable when dried seeds have been stored in presumed constant conditions for a period of two or three years and samples withdrawn at about monthly intervals and germinated under the same carefully controlled environmental conditions may be explained simply as growth responses to the month by month systematic variations in the ambient subtle geophysical conditions. It does not demand, as many students of biological clocks have chosen to assume it must, that each individual seed contain its own independent timing system inexorably measuring off periods, year after year. Ingrained knowledge of the sequence of events in these natural environmental cycles could account for the well-known capacity of organisms to display anticipatory adaptive behavior in relation to the external cyclic events.

Links have now been securely forged between living organisms and the fluctuating electromagnetic forces of their environment. We cannot gainsay that the living organism is as sensitive a receiving system as the composite of all man's artificial electronic equipment by which he gains geophysical and astrophysical information. Geophysicists are now busily unraveling the multiplicity of ways in which variations in these atmospheric forces are related to the activities and movements of the earth, sun, moon, and planets, and even the distant stars. Now, tied to their continuing discoveries are the paralleling, inescapable questions of possible biological significances.

Man did not arise on planet earth abruptly and *de novo*. He came gradually to what he is through an orderly transformation, beginning probably from chance chemical complexes in the warm primeval oceans as first life arose as primordial bits of slime. It is only fitting, therefore, that we seek man's cosmic roots in his long evolutionary past. Biological clocks geared to the major cosmic periodicities appear omnipresent in living creatures. Their occurrence ranges from unicellular forms and flowering plants to mammals, including man. This indicates the ancient, deep-seated character of the relationship of man to the Universe.

When we look further and observe celestial navigation in animals as diverse as the insects and crustaceans, on the one hand, and the fishes and birds, on the other, we see again an ancient cosmic relationship. The common ancestry of these two widely different kinds of creatures harks back probably to well over a billion years. At that early age either the eyes of the organisms were already turning skyward to seek assistance in the satisfaction of demands imposed by their earthly lives or the propensity or potentiality for doing so was already present and unfolding. With such deep roots of celestial relations in the ancestry of man, it is perhaps not difficult to understand why, as reasoning evolved, he should try to derive further assistance from the skies.

A very challenging and exciting new area of science has thus now appeared on the scene. How are terrestrial creatures, animals and plants and even man himself, influenced by these subtle cosmic fluctuations? Man is unquestionably and inextricably linked by many threads with the rest of the Universe, not only by way of the physical instruments he has invented and constructed, but also by way of the amazing sensitivities of his own living substance. Michel Gauquelin has splendidly brought a brief outline of the history of the subject into focus in a single picture, something only a person who has devoted many years of study and critical contemplation to it, one whose own investigations have suggested the most awe-inspiring, exciting, and thought-provoking celestial relationships yet reported for man himself, could have done.

FRANK A. BROWN, JR.
Morrison Professor of Biology
Northwestern University
Evanston, Illinois

Contents

Genetic Knowledge • A Sacrilegious Hypothesis •
A Bold Experiment • The Biological Compass •
Electrical Perception • Gravitational Perception
• Subtle Rhythms

The Adventure of Drs. Faure and Sardou •
Tchijevsky's History • Takata's History • The
Story of Nicolas Schulz • Dr. De Rudder's Ques-
tion • Infarction of the Myocardium • Tubercu-
losis • Effects on the Nervous System • "Lunacy"
• Biology and the Moon • The Menstrual Cycle
• The Unknown Senses of Man • Magnetic Man

Importance of the Month of Birth • Month of
Birth and Body Build • Month of Birth and In-
telligence • A Twenty-four-hour Rhythm of
Birth • The Great Midwife? • Birth and the
Lunar Day

The Medical Stars • The Schedule of Success •
Looking for an Explanation • Variable Levels of
Sensitivity • A Genetic Theory • Magnetic In-
fluences • The Child and Uniform Conditions •
Toward a Practical Application

The Freezing Point of Water • A Parenthesis •
Simple Witchcraft? • The Method of Chemical
Tests • The Structure of Water • The Cosmos
Upsets the Structure of Water • The Cosmic
Basis of Life

Introduction

THE SUBJECT of this book is the effect the
cosmos has on human life; it is a subject that has always
haunted man's imagination. We will follow the history
of the ideas that have been accepted in succession, from
the first astrological models to the most recent discoveries of modern science. A basic contradiction seems to exist between the magical interpretations of the past centuries and current rational explanations; yet in reality,
despite the obvious differences, they are joined by a deep
consistency. Man himself created this unity through his
constant search for an answer to the secret of his place
in the universe.

People of centuries past felt that they were but play-
things among the cosmic forces surrounding them. To reduce their anxiety, and to give a meaning to their existence, they had to try to understand the laws ruling these
forces. About five thousand years ago, the Chaldeans
solved the problem to their satisfaction, and the astrological conception of cosmic influences was born. Chaldean astrology used magic as an explanation and saw in
the position of the planet a clue to the prediction of the
future. Such an interpretation was strangely adapted to
man's thinking. The succeeding civilizations of Greece

and Rome, instead of abandoning such magic beliefs, went on to develop and codify them.

After the barbarian invasions that destroyed the Roman Empire, the fire of astrology seemed to have been extinguished. But it was slowly burning under the ashes: in the fifteenth century, the Italian Renaissance fanned the fires higher than ever. Great thinkers picked up the scientific problems where they had been abandoned by the ancients. In astronomy—the sister of astrology—success was total: Copernicus displaced the earth from the center of the universe, Tycho Brahe computed the planetary orbits with a precision undreamed of before, Kepler discovered the laws of planetary motions that replaced the hoary systems of the past, Galileo in studying sunspots undermined the belief in the changelessness of heavenly bodies, and finally Newton established the law of universal gravitation, which prepared the way for the great synthesis that Einstein achieved at the beginning of the twentieth century. All these great men were also concerned with the astrological conception of the world. More than anyone else, Kepler hoped to forge a new astrology, to parallel the progress of astronomy. But his attempt failed, because he could not abandon his fascination with the possibility of predicting from the movement of the stars. Astrology thus fell back into superstition. It was rejected by the universities, and scientists lost interest in it. At the same time, its popularity increased with the masses. In the middle of the twentieth century it has more than ever degenerated into fortune telling, shamelessly exploited by charlatans. Yet sociological surveys show that about half of the people believe in horoscopes to some extent. The falsity of such a belief must certainly be exposed.

But beyond the outmoded superstition, sensible thinkers intuitively reasoned that there must be some cosmic influences affecting human life. This intuition is, and has always been, essentially correct. The error has been in trying to explain cosmic actions in terms of occult characteristics, which the heavenly bodies obviously cannot possess. This error, however, need not be continued.

Today the cosmos is fashionable. Thanks to advances in astrophysics, humans are being sent into space. Yet we barely know the laws governing the influences of space on man. In the entire history of thought, there are only a few examples of such an astonishing contradiction. All this must change. In the last few years, researchers have begun to fill in the void left by astrology's departure from the scientific scene. Modern scientists have finally been able to ask the old question in a more meaningful way: How are the cosmic clocks related to the biological rhythms of living organisms? The success or failure of space travel may depend on the answer to this question.

NASA has concerned itself with a fascinating proposal suggested by Frank A. Brown, Morrison Professor of Biology at Northwestern University. It consists in transporting across space for a prolonged period of time a variety of organisms, beginning with simple plants. The construction of a "potato space-cabin" will be the first step. What will happen to the tubers as they travel through space for an indeterminate period of time? Perhaps nothing. But if the potatoes were to die, according to Eugene R. Spangler, a biologist affiliated with the American Institute of Aeronautics, it would mean that prolonged space travel on man's part would also be dangerous. Why? Because this project, facetiously nicknamed "Spudnik I," deals with a fundamental issue. The problem it tries to resolve is whether the cosmic clocks that set the

pace to the rhythm of earthly life—the movements
of the sun, the moon, and the planets—are indispensable
to all biological life. Perhaps if the rhythm is drastically
altered, the potato will not be able to adapt. And since
man is much more sensitive than a plant, it becomes essential to know if man can leave the rhythms of his earthly
environment for a prolonged period of time without suffering, as a result, grave consequences.

It is this problem that has finally aroused scientists to
fathom the cosmic influences that for six thousand years
have been waiting to be systematically investigated. Yet
space travel did not begin with the first astronaut; we
have always been traveling in a spaceship. For a long time
man had been unaware of this fact, since conditions on
earth are apparently more comfortable than inside a
space capsule; but by now we all know that our spaceship, the earth, hurtles unceasingly through interstellar
space. In the words of Giorgio Piccardi, head of the Institute for Physical Chemistry at the University of Florence:
"To be subjected to cosmic effects, man does not have
to be shot into space; he does not even have to leave his
home. Man is always surrounded by the universe, since
the universe is everywhere."

The cosmos around us is neither changeless nor empty.
The artificial satellites have shown clearly that space is
filled with an infinity of corpuscles and waves buffeting
our earth, affecting everything that lives on its surface.
In the thirty years or so that researchers have studied
the matter scientifically, strange relationships between
life and the universe have been discovered. Step by step,
working its way in the shadow of established disciplines,
a new science is emerging. The most important part of
this book is devoted to an account of the conquests in
this new branch of human understanding.

In the first place, there are the amazing links that relate man to the sun. The latter is not, as the Pythagoreans imagined, a motionless golden sphere; it gets covered with spots, it erupts in huge explosions. And the waves of these cataclysmic changes reverberate among us. Today the moon, always surrounded by legendary beliefs, begins to reveal its true secrets. Professor Brown charted the moon's effect on lower forms of life and found that several animal species are sensitive to its mysterious messages. Previously unknown sensory receptors have been discovered among all forms of life, including man, senses that allow the organism to receive such messages and to set its behavior on the beam of cosmic clocks.

Next comes a very old question, one that originated with the first dreams of mankind: Does the cosmos influence all men in a similar way? The astrologers, who had formulated this question naively, were unable to provide a satisfying answer. Scientists today hope to have found a better one. The marvelously intricate human machinery seems to be sensitive to extremely subtle cosmic influences radiating from the planets close to our earth. Recently a new phenomenon, which we have called "planetary heredity," has been uncovered: as a function of its genetic constitution, the human organism at birth receives the cosmic messages in a specific, personal way. It may appear incredible that living organisms should be able to perceive the infinitely weak actions of the planetary bodies. How this is possible has been indicated by Piccardi, the founder of a new discipline, cosmic chemistry. He has shown that the cosmos affects man through the mediating effect of water, the liquid so necessary for the existence of life on our planet. Water has strange physical properties that connect us intimately and permanently with cosmic forces. Thanks to cosmic chemistry, what only a short time ago was incomprehensible is now beginning to be conceivable.

Astrology, the ancient universal religion, the primitive majestic effort toward a cosmic synthesis, has fallen completely into the hands of charlatans. A new science has been born in its place. This science should not be scornful of the past; after all, we owe the birth of astronomy to the astrological concern of our predecessors. It is only poetic justice that this science, in its maturity, and after a two-thousand-year detour, should help to discover the true links that tie man to the universe.

CHRONOLOGY

25,000–10,000 B.C. (approximately)	The notches on the bones of reindeer and the tusks of mammoths represent the phases of the moon.
6000 B.C.	The beginning of the observation of the sky by the Sumerians.
3000 B.C.	Astrological predictions of Sargon the Old.
2073 B.C.	Chounn, the first emperor of China, makes a sacrifice to the "seven rectors" (the planets).
1800 B.C.	Construction of the megaliths of Stonehenge, near Salisbury (Southern England).
Fourteenth century B.C.	The great Sumerian gods are Sin, the Moon god; Shamash, the Sun god; and Ishtar, the goddess of Venus.
1375 B.C.	Hymn to the sun by Pharaoh Ikhnaton.
700–400 B.C.	Discovery and description of the zodiac by the Babylonians.
Sixth century B.C.	Doctrine of the harmony of the spheres by Pythagoras (Samos, Greece).
Fifth century B.C.	First astrological maxims in Chaldea based on the birth of the king.
409 B.C.	Date of the oldest known Babylonian horoscope.
331 B.C.	Conquest of Chaldea by Alexander the Great.
280 B.C.	Publication of *Babyloniaca* by Berossus, priest of Marduk in Babylon.
220 B.C.	The Greek Carneades criticizes astrology in the name of reason.
70 B.C.	The first Greek horoscopes which take into account the precise hour of birth.
40 B.C.	Cicero publishes *On Divinations*, in which he exposes the principal scientific criticisms of astrology.

30 B.C.	The Emperor Augustus has his horoscope read by the astrologer Thrasyllus. His successors follow his example.
10 AD.	Publication of the *Astronomicon* by Manilius, the first Greek work on astrology.
140 A.D.	Publication of *Tetrabiblos* by Ptolemy, the most famous work on astrology.
Fourth century A.D.	Saint Augustine criticizes astrology in the name of the Christian faith, in his *Confessions*.
700–1200 A.D.	Islam perpetuates the ancient astrological tradition.
1400–1600 A.D.	In the Aztec religion of Mexico, Quetzaltcoalt, the feathered serpent, is regarded as the lord of the planet Venus.
1543 A.D.	With the publication of Copernicus' *De Revolutionibus Orbium Caelestium,* the earth is no longer regarded as the center of the universe.
1555 A.D.	The first edition of Nostradamus' prophecies (Lyon, France).
1571–1630 A.D.	The life of Johannes Kepler, who discovered the laws of motion of the planets and actively pursued the creation of a new astrology.
1666 A.D.	Official condemnation of astrology by Colbert, Minister of Louis XIV, in France. Astrology is banished from the Academy of Sciences and from the university.
1749–1832 A.D.	The life of the great poet Goethe, who pursued astrology.
1828 A.D.	The English astrologer Raphael publishes his *Manual of Astrology.*
1898 A.D.	The scholarly Swede Svante Arrhenius, winner of the Nobel Prize in physics, undertakes the first statistical work on the influence of the moon on the weather and on living beings.

1920 A.D.   Renewal of the horoscope. Great success of the charlatans, helped by the development of communications media.

1920–1940 A.D.   A.L. Tchijevsky's statistical work on the role of sunspots on human life.

1922 A.D.   Memorandum from Doctors Faure and Sardou to the Academy of Sciences concerning the influence of sunspots on sudden illnesses.

1938 A.D.   Publication of *Season of Birth* by E. Huntington.

1939–1945 A.D.   The Nazis try to interpret the prophecies of Nostradamus in their favor.

1941 A.D.   The Japanese Maki Takata demonstrates the role of an unknown solar ray on human blood serum.

1948 A.D.   Frank A. Brown discovers mysterious exogenous rhythms in plants and animals.

1950 A.D.   Giorgio Piccardi begins work on the relation between the cosmos and chemical tests.

1950–1955 A.D.   Publication by scientists of statistics demonstrating the falsity of horoscopes.

1957 A.D.   Satellites are launched into space and demonstrate many hitherto unknown interactions between the bodies of the solar system.

1960 A.D.   First studies indicating a correlation between planets and heredity revealed.

1963 A.D.   Survey by the French Institute of Public Opinion reveals that despite the efforts of scientists, 43 per cent of the population still believes that astrology is a true science.

PART
One

The Oldest Religion

WHERE did astrology originate? The answer is: everywhere on earth. When did it begin? It has existed as long as man has—in fact, even longer. When the sun goes into eclipse, animals become restless and anxious; they seem to fear an imminent danger. Birds cease to sing, and apes leave their trees, banding together for safety, keeping silence.

Astrology was born from the encounter between an intelligence only dimly capable of representing the world to itself and the fear that such a world inspired. For the primitive man, the sky was filled with marvelous and awesome wonders. This fear and admiration were not unjustified: the power of the skies was very real. The earliest human civilizations relied on herding, farming, fishing, or hunting and were thus at the mercy of the vagaries of nature. The sky would fill with clouds, lightning would dart through space, and thunder would roll. Rain would follow the wind, and the harvests would be destroyed. If the skies remained serene, drought would dry the crops and invite the plague of migrant locusts. In winter the freezing air would turn the quenching drops of rain into little dancing crystals that covered the countryside with a thick white mantle.

As far back in time as we can go, we find records of man's efforts in questioning the skies. Alexander Marshack, writing in the November 6, 1964, issue of *Science,* contends that nicks cut in certain reindeer bones and mammoth ivory in the Upper Paleolithic period represent notations of lunar sequences. Thus, some ten thousand to twenty-five thousand years ago man may have been observing and reporting the cycles of the moon.[1]

Ten miles from Salisbury, in the south of England, rises Stonehenge, a strange assembly of twelve-foot-high menhirs surrounded by fifty-six pits known as Aubrey's holes. This structure is thought to date back to about 1800 B.C. Professor G.S. Hawkins of Boston University, with the help of an IBM machine, has shown that these crude ruins can be used to record the positions of the sun and of the moon with amazing precision—plus or minus one degree of the circle.[2] There is less than one probability in a million that the correlation he found is due to random chance. Hawkins writes:

> The Aubrey holes provided a system for counting the years, one hole for each year, to aid in predicting the movements of the Moon. Perhaps cremations were performed in a particular Aubrey hole during the course of the year, or perhaps the hole was marked by a movable stone. Stonehenge can be used as a gigantic digital computer.[3]

It seems, then, that Stonehenge was a kind of Bronze Age observatory in which priests announced the coming of the seasons and the eclipses of the sun and the moon. This scientific activity was in no way incompatible with the religious rituals that also took place there; in fact, the two reinforced each other.

Stonehenge shows the two main kinds of concerns our ancestors felt when they looked up to the skies: scientific and religious. The world, whether friendly or hostile, was always indispensable; primitive man knew he had to control it somehow. In order to do this he could try two things: to worship it or to know it. Astrology was born as a way of combining these two attempts to establish some measure of control over the world. It is no exaggeration to say, as most historians do, that astrology was at the same time the first religion and the first science man developed.

The sun, the moon, the stars—all celestial bodies became objects of worship, of fear, of hope. Their influence seemed to affect not only the fate of men but also the future of the world, both threatening its destruction and promising its rebirth. They affected the rains, the soothing winds, earthquakes, unforeseeable catastrophes. This syncretistic belief, which naively expresses the ceaseless interaction between the cosmos and terrestrial life, is found among all primitive peoples.

The Sun

The sun's return each morning, its "rebirth" after its "death" on the previous evening, was greeted with ritual worship by the oldest peoples we have records of, and it is still so greeted in primitive societies:

> Red Indian mothers hold their newly-born babies out to the sun. Among the Navajos the young girls reaching the age of puberty have to prepare a huge cake; while it is baking they have to run towards the rising sun and back, wearing full ceremonial dress. Saluting the rising sun was a common practice. Greeks like Socrates and Dion followed it; so did the Chinese, the Japanese and the Indian Brahmins.[4]

In Egypt, the pharaoh Amenophis IV took the name of Ikhnaton in honor of the sun; the name means "ray of the sun's face." In 1375 B.C. he composed a famous hymn of worship to Aton, "the great living circle of the Sun":

> This only god has made the distant earth, men,
> birds, and animals. . . . When he shows himself, all
> flowers grow and live on; the fields blossom when he
> raises and rejoice at his sight; all beasts spring up to
> greet him and the birds in the marshes beat their
> wings.[5]

Buried under their giant pyramids, the bodies of the
pharaohs Cheops, Chephren, and Mycerinos were expected to share in the sun's eternal life. The pyramids
themselves were symbols of the sun. The facade closest
to each grave's entrance is perfectly oriented toward the
rising sun. For the great pyramid of Cheops the error is
only three degrees of arc, which is almost incredible. In
Abou-Simbel, on a certain date, the sun's rays find their
way into the very pit of Ramses II's grave. "The great
pyramids, as well as the small golden ones placed on the
tip of the obelisks, were representations of the sun's rays
descending down to the earth."[6]

The setting of the sun god was by contrast a sad event.
The sun descended to the "land of the dead." Any man
it took along on this journey would not return. Thus the
belief, found everywhere from New Zealand to the New
Hebrides, that one glance at the setting sun could cause
a man's death.[7] But at the same time, the sun could also
escort the souls of the dead across the infernal regions
and bring them back the next morning with the light of
the day.

The Moon

The behavior of the moon, even stranger than that of
the sun, was a great cause of puzzlement to the first observers:

The moon, too, moved across the sky among the stars, which it overtook night after night, while its appearance underwent a mysterious change from a feeble sickle in the evening sky to the shining disc of the full moon dominating the night and illuminating the earth until it began to wane and turned again into a narrow sliver which vanished at dawn. This process continually repeated itself in a cycle apparently equivalent to the menstrual period of women.[8]

Everywhere on earth the moon has been linked to the same cosmic processes: rain, plants, and animal fertility. These correspondences are present

> even in such archaic and uncontaminated religions as that of the Pygmies. The feast for the new moon among African Pygmies takes place just before the beginning of the rainy season. The moon, which they call Pe, is believed to be the "principle of generation and mother of fertility."[9]

For the Papuans, "the moon is a girl's first husband. They assume that menstruation is a proof of the relations between women and the moon."[10]

Among the Hittites, the moon was called Arma, which means big, pregnant. In India it was held to be king of everything that grows on the earth and protector of all living things. Its waning was considered to be a real sickness. In Cambodia the full moon marked the turning point for good luck, the summit on which all changes stood in balance.

In ancient Egypt, the moon's influence was present everywhere: several of the gods were thought to represent it. Its waxing was called "the opening of Horus' eye." When the eye of the hawk-god was completely open, the moon was full. The twenty-eight-day lunar cycle was compared to a staircase with fourteen steps: first one ascended the staircase to the "fullness of the eye," then one went down it until the eye closed. This stood for the fourteen days during which the moon waxes, then the fourteen days of waning till the new moon. Lunar eclipses were considered to be evil omens presaging sad events. Often the moon itself was seen as dangerous. Its crescent was sometimes seen as a knife, "a golden sickle in the starry field." An Egyptian manuscript asks: "Isn't the moon a knife? It can therefore punish those who are guilty."[11]

The Stars

The principal stars and constellations have also been worshiped. Their shapes and their movements have given rise to numerous myths and rituals. In China

the Great Bear or Wain [Big Dipper] is worshiped as a propitious deity. Women who wish to have children pray to it. A bridal crown displays the Great Bear in pearls and emeralds. An ancient picture of the Han dynasty about the beginning of our era shows the Great Bear as a ruler in a chariot with various spirits doing homage.[12]

In Pomerania they still tell the following story:

The Great Bear is also called Dümkt. Dümkt was a wicked farmer who used his people and his cattle most cruelly. As a punishment he was placed in the heavens after his death. There he drives in the same wild way he did when on earth. Three horses draw his wagon, and Dümkt rides on the middle one, but the whole group is all awry, as though it were about to fall over any moment.[13]

In Egypt the Nile, which provided the livelihood for the whole country, was considered a god of fertility:

But was it not the sky that caused the beneficial growth of the river? Each year, the waters increased when the brilliant star Sirius rose at the same time that the sun did. This suggested that the floods of the Nile were due to the alliance between the propitious actions of the sun and Sirius—an alliance that occurred only once a year. It was the time when the parched soil of Egypt revived. This is why the Egyptians' New Year was held on the date that Sirius rose with the sun.[14]

The seven stars of the Pleiades have been worshiped throughout history. The Greeks named them after the seven daughters of Atlas who killed themselves and were changed into stars. A Danish folk tale explains why the constellation is invisible during part of the year in this way:

> Once upon a time, there was a girl who had seven illegitimate children. A man met her and said to her, "Good day to you, you and your seven bastards!" To punish him, God changed the man into a cuckoo. The children were turned into angels and placed in the sky. During the season in summer when the cuckoo calls, the Pleiades are invisible.[15]

Among the Aztecs of Central America, the Pleiades were used as a pretext for horrifying rituals. The stars' passage across the meridian signaled the beginning of human sacrifices:

> Deep in their souls the ancient Mexicans could not trust the future. Their world was too fragile, always exposed to a catastrophe. Every fifty-two years the people of the whole empire succumbed to terror, fearing that the last sunset of their "century" would not be followed by a new dawn. The fires were extinguished in the towns and in the countryside, while terror-stricken crowds thronged to the foothills of Mount

Ulxachtecatl. On its summit, the priests were watching
the constellation of the Pleiades. The astronomer-priest
gave a signal: a prisoner was stretched out on the altar,
a stone knife was plunged into his breast with a dull
noise, and over the gaping wound a burning stick was
waved. And lo! The flame would flicker, as if born from
the broken breast, and among joyful clamor, messen-
gers lit torches and left to spread the sacred fire to the
four corners of the central valley. Thus the world had
once more escaped destruction.[16]

Indian Religions

Since the first dawn of history, human thought has
been dominated by the belief that astral movements are
related to all earthly phenomena, that they rule farming,
husbandry, health, and the social order. Berthelot has
called this belief astrobiology. The great religions of
mankind are still permeated by such primitive astrology.
The ancient texts of India and China are good illustra-
tions of this statement.

One can easily discover astrological ideas in Hindu
religious writing. The Vedas set the dates for sacrifices
at the new and at the full moon. The celestial bodies are
the guardians of *rita*, which is a union of the cosmic and
the social orders: "Across the sky runs the twelve-fold
path of *rita*, which never grows old: the year."

> For Vedic man sky and earth, forest and mountain,
> the waters of seas and rivers, plants and animals, are
> all inhabited by the spirit of cosmic forces led by the
> powerful personality of Indra, god of thunder and
> lightning, who rules from his throne in the clouds.
> Under him are the eight Adityas, the celestial bodies
> who are sons of the goddess Aditi. They include Mitra-
> Varuna, the primal couple, representing the earth and

the sky; then the five planets, and Surya, the sun. Ushan, the dawn, each morning lightly walks to the East to open the heavenly doors so that her lover, Surya, can enter; each evening Ratri closes them again, ushering in his domain, the night.[17]

In the Upanishads, Brahma is called "the ruling breath of the cosmos." Shiva's well-known cosmic dance, so often represented in sculpture, symbolizes the rhythmic movement of the universe, to which man can associate himself through the dance. The swastika, or hooked-cross, is also an ancient cosmic and religious symbol in India. It represents the circular course of the sun around the four points of the compass.

Chinese Philosophy

In China, "the cosmic rhythms reveal order, harmony, permanence, and fertility. The cosmos in its entirety is a living, real, and sacred organism."[18] More than two thousand years before Christ astrology was the basis of the established order. The emperor's title was "Son of the Heavens." One of his main functions was to assure good relations between heavenly motions and human affairs. He was the object of astrological predictions and performed sacrifices to the gods in the skies:

> The oldest known mention of these sacrifices is found in the Bamboo Annals, a very old manuscript discovered in a princely grave in the year 281 A.D. It mentions that in 2073 B.C., when Chounn succeeded Yao, the first historical emperor of China, he inaugurated his rule by offering a sacrifice to the "Sovereign of the Sky." He then visited the four sacred mountains located at the four points of the compass, surveyed the propitious position of the "Seven Rectors" (the sun, moon,

and five planets), and made an offering to the "Six Meteors" (the wind, clouds, thunder, rain, cold, and warmth).[19]

The great Chinese religions are as imbued with astrological notions as the Emperor himself was. To this effect Confucius says: "He who rules by means of virtue is like the Pole star which stays motionless in its place, while all the other stars turn around it." Another Chinese moralist advises, "Love everything in the universe, because the sun and the earth are but one body."

Kouan-Tsé, a famous Taoist writer, said: "The Tao [way] which is revealed by the sun's course through the heavens is also revealed inside man's heart. . . . It is the vital energy which lends existence to being. On earth it makes the five crops grow; up high, it orders the path of the stars." The Tao is therefore the vital energy of the whole universe, and of man as well. In China, as in India and in some other cultures as well, the air was believed to be filled with grains of life descending from heaven, and for this reason breathing exercises were held to be important.

Such a theory, linking the macrocosm (the universe) to the microcosm (the human body), had some practical applications. As the famous Orientalist Henri Maspero explained:

> Taoist magicians in the first centuries of our era thought that in the various parts of the human body there lived gods who at the same time were also gods of the heavens, of earth, of the constellations, of the mountains, and of the rivers. Through meditation one could see the cosmic gods living outside the body, and one was allowed thus to learn from them the psychophysiological precepts of moral sanity and health, which enabled one to chase from one's body evil spirits

and evil influences. By feeding on "breath" rather than coarse food one could be purified; by exposing oneself to sunshine or to the light of the moon one could be filled with celestial influences. Thus purified and strengthened, one was able to ascend to the heavens, where one could taste eternal life with body and soul.[20]

In all these religions the main concern is to harmonize man with the cosmos, with space and time. These systems are as strangely similar in substance as they are varied in form. This is why one has to speak not of one astrobiology but of many: the Egyptian, the Mexican, the Indian, the Chinese. But none of these really deals with astrology, that is, a foretelling by means of the stars. Among all these ancient religions, only one, which embodied what we now call astrology, has survived to our days: the Chaldean view of the universe.

NOTES TO CHAPTER ONE

1. "The Compleat Calendar," *The Sciences*, IV (1965), No. 8, 1.
2. G. S. Hawkins, *Stonehenge Decoded* (New York: Doubleday, 1965).
3. ———, "Stonehenge: A Neolithic Computer," *Nature*, CCII (1964), 1258.
4. E. Zinner, *The Stars Above Us* (London: Allen and Unwin, 1957).
5. R. Berthelot, *La pensée de l'Asie et l'Astrobiologie* (Paris: Payot, 1949).
6. *Ibid.*
7. M. Eliade, *Traité d'histoire des religions* (Paris: Payot, 1959).
8. Zinner, *op. cit.*
9. Trilles, *Les pygmées de la forêt équatoriale* (Paris: 1933).
10. Eliade, *op. cit.*
11. *La lune, mythes et rites* (Paris: Le Seuil, 1962).
12. Zinner, *op cit.*
13. *Ibid.*
14. M. Gauquelin, *L'astrologie devant la science* (Paris: Planète, 1965).
15. Zinner, *op. cit.*
16. J. Soustelle, *La vie quotidienne des Aztèques* (Paris: Hachette, 1959).
17. A. Migot, "Cinq millénaires d'astrologie," *Janus*, No. 8 (1965), 53.
18. M. Eliade, *Le sacré et le profane* (Paris: N.R.F., 1965).
19. Migot, *op. cit.*
20. Berthelot, *op. cit.*

The Oldest Science

In BABYLON, the ancient empire of Mesopotamia, far above the bustle of the city, were located the observatories, magic watchtowers from which priests studied the motion of the stars night and day, without interruption. These towers were called ziggurats, or "cosmic mountains." The ones in Ur, Uruk, and Babylon were supposed to be about 270 feet high. They had seven terraces, built one on the other, to represent the seven planetary heavens. By climbing to the top, a priest could reach the summit of the universe as it was conceived by the Chaldeans. This presumptuous belief was exposed to ridicule in the Bible through the legend of the Tower of Babel (Babylon's ancient name), which was to reach to the sky. The priests, who mediated between the heavens and the King, had to observe the celestial course of the stars in order to know the will of the gods. Thus was astrology born five thousand years ago in Chaldea.

Astrology was the first science of the sky. It was imbued with magic, without doubt, but it was a science nevertheless. The Chaldeans developed the zodiacal system, which astronomers still use; they recognized the planets in the midst of the fixed stars. But at the same time they attributed to the zodiacal signs and to stars a power over the destinies of man. Little clay tablets inscribed in cuneiform script, still intact today, have preserved a number of systematically codified predictions. These are the first elements of astrology. Thus at the beginning of its long journey, "science emerges in the shape of Janus, the two-faced god, guardian of doors and gates: the face in front alert and observant, while the other, dreamy and glassy-eyed, stares in the opposite direction."[1]

The Chaldeans' astronomical discoveries and their astrological transcriptions were a fundamental breakthrough. Thanks to the imaginative and patient work of many Orientalists, in particular A. Sachs and B. Van der Waerden, the clay tablets have revealed their secrets, enabling us to sketch in the development of Chaldean astrology.

The Heavenly Signs

On today's map, Chaldea would occupy approximately the area of Iraq. Many civilizations have succeeded each other in this part of the world. More than six thousand years ago it was inhabited by the Sumerians, a people of shepherds and farmers. They worshiped above all the vital forces of fertility. They were also aware of the mysterious link between the yearly cycles of growth and the cycles of the sky: the harvests followed the seasons, and the seasons followed the motion of the sun. And then, of course, there was the moon, whose appearance in the evening skies brought with it the sweetness of the night and rest after the burning daylight. There was also "a great female god, daughter or bride of the sky; she was soon taken to be the goddess of fertility."[2] Her home was thought to be on the planet Venus. "The great triad in that country was Sin the moon-god, who was masculine and the most powerful, Shamash the sun-god, feminine, and Ishtar, the goddess of love. Symbols of all three appear in stone carvings from the 14th century B.C."[3]

Sin was pictured as a strong man with a beard of lapis-lazuli who traveled across the sky in his boat, the lunar crescent. Shamash, his child, ruled the year, determining its length by circling the heavens in 365 days. Ishtar shed her light from the brilliant planet Venus.

The Babylonians, who succeeded the Sumerians, developed the art of prediction to a considerable extent. Every method for telling the future was attempted. "The information we ask today of scientists in control of complicated instruments was once asked of the Babylonian priests. Divination was an official procedure."[4] Some of the forms by which the future was predicted included dreams, the analysis of animal livers, abnormal births, the flight of birds, or bodily symptoms. For instance, a clay tablet instructs: "When a man's right ear whistles, it is a sign that a magic spell has seized him."[5] However, the really great events were recorded in the sky. The heavenly signs were held to be the most important. To rule the country well one had to be able to predict their motions, and to do that one must study the celestial cycles; the return of the same pattern of stars meant the recurrence of events previously associated with that pattern. This pressing need explains the Chaldeans' discovery of the movement of the skies.

The Origin of the Zodiac

The Chaldean priest-astronomers divided the sky into three large strips, which they called "the heavenly paths": in the middle was Anu's way, flanked by the paths of Enlil and Ea. As they kept watch night and day, they finally realized that both the sun and the moon always kept moving along Anu's way. Thus they attached a special importance to the strip of the sky the two great gods chose for their journeys. The constellations the sun and the moon crossed on their way also acquired a special meaning for the Chaldeans.

Anu's way was nothing other than the first version of the zodiac astronomers use today: a space sixteen degrees wide, which contains the constantly repeated path of the sun, the moon, and the planets. The Chaldeans observed this pattern very accurately. Van der Waerden, a specialist in cuneiform texts, writes in his *History of the Zodiac:*

> The zodiacal belt with its constellations was known in Babylonia as early as 700 B.C. The first tablet of the series *MulApin* lists "the constellations in the path of the moon" as follows:

> the hair bush = Pleiades
> the bull of Anu = Taurus
> Anu's true shepherd = Orion
> the old man = Perseus
> sickle sword = Auriga
> the great twins = Gemini
> Prokyon or Cancer
> lion or lioness = Leo
> furrow = Spica
> the scales = Libra
> scorpion = Scorpio
> archer = Sagittarius
> goatfish = Capricornus
> great star or giant = Aquarius
> the tails = Pisces
> the great swallow = Pegasi
> the Goddess Anunitum = Pisces + middle part of
>   Andromedes
> the hireling = Aries

As a matter of fact, all constellations mentioned belong to the zodiacal belt, with the exception of Orion, Perseus, and Auriga.[6]

Soon afterward the twelve signs appeared, in the same forms known to us today. They are first mentioned in the document VAT 4924, dated 419 B.C., with the names of Aries, Pleiades, Gemini, Praesepe, Leo, Spica, Libra, Scorpio, Sagittarius, Capricornus, Aquarius, and Pisces. As Van der Waerden noted, these "Babylonian signs are of strictly equal length"—just as today. It was a remarkably abstract framework for observation. The only change in nomenclature occurred when the Greeks substituted Taurus, Cancer, and Virgo for Pleiades, Praesepe, and Spica.[7] Sachs mentions in this context that "the invention of the zodiac which turned out to be so fruitful for astronomy and astrology is one indication of the new, adventuresome spirit of this period (600-300 B.C.)."[8]

The names of the twelve signs were given to the star-clusters in Anu's path according to several magic rules. The fantastic mythology of the Babylonians, first described in the famous *Epic of Creation,* supplied the odd creatures. But why twelve signs? Van der Waerden claims that they originally corresponded to the twelve months of the Babylonian calendar: "The idea of some correspondence of months to constellations is very old. It goes back to the so-called Astrolabe lists (1100 B.C. or earlier)."[9] But the use of the zodiac did not remain limited to the calendar; its influence expanded with time. Each of its signs was assumed to exercise precise influences over the earth. The rules by which predictions were made were a mixture of observations and analogies. For instance, the shape of Scorpio reminded the Chaldean priest of the hated insect whose pincers seemed to be

marked in the sky by two brilliant stars. The celestial
Scorpio was held to be just as fearsome as the poisonous
scorpion of the desert: "If Mars approaches Scorpio, the
King must die of the bite of this insect."[10] Spica, or fur-
row (which was later to become the sign of Virgo), was
related to the harvest. The Chaldeans harvested in February, a time when Spica was "the sign that rose smiling
on the farmers as soon as the sun set."[11]

W. Peuckert proposed an explanation for the influence of the sign of Pisces:

> It was believed that during a year when fish failed to
> spawn normally, the constellation of Pisces (fish) was
> shining feebly. Therefore they thought they saw in this
> a cause, and made up the formula: when Pisces is dim,
> the spawning is bad.[12]

Similarly, the position of Libra (scales) influenced the
weight of wheat and the price of crops. One could also
add that the signs corresponding to the winter season
in our hemisphere, a period of frequent rains, are all
related to water: Capricorn (goat-fish), Aquarius, and
Pisces are in the sun's path between December 20 and
March 20.

Through the centuries, the meanings associated with
the signs of the constellations in the yearly path traversed
by the sun became more and more precise. When Alexander the Great conquered Chaldea in 331 B.C., the
Greeks took over the whole system and codified it according to the pattern still in use. We will return to that
period in the next chapter.

The Bright Ones

As they scanned Anu's way, the priests noticed that
there were some stars that moved along the zodiac just
as the sun and moon did. These mysterious objects, which

shone brighter than most stars, were the planets. Because of their strange behavior they were given the name *bibbu*, or "wild goats"—as opposed to the quiet, sheepish flock of fixed stars, which always kept their place in the firmament. Not only did the *bibbu* pass across the constellations as did Sin and Shamash, their course was highly irregular: one would stop, or even retrace its path on Anu's way, and then stand still for a few months before resuming its progress. Modern astronomy has explained the planets' "change in speed" as an optical illusion: "It is the yearly orbit of the earth that changes the perspective of the planets seen against the far background of the constellations. The speed of the earth combined with the planet's own speed will determine the latter's apparent motion."[13] But it was only the apparent motion that the Chaldeans saw, and they were fascinated. The planets behaved as if they had life: they were obviously the dwellings of gods whose appearance in the sky announced either favorable or unfavorable intentions. So each planet was linked to a god carefully chosen from Chaldean mythology. The nomenclature had nothing to do with chance. It was chosen

> on the basis of imagined similarities between the brilliance, the color, the position, the behavior, I was going to say the customs, of these wandering planets —kings of the stars—and the characteristics of the gods created by the same imagination.[14]

Venus, the brightest planet, received her attributes first. She was, as we have seen, the home of Ishtar, goddess of fertility and fecundity from the most ancient times. The priests had some difficulty in following Mercury, since that planet, the closest to the sun, is often hidden by the latter's stronger light. The Chaldeans held it to be the dwelling of Nebo, a god who was untrustworthy, shy, shrewd, and voluble. The planet Mars became the home of Nergal, the dangerous, evil, and violent god of war. Its reddish light and sudden changes in direction did not favorably impress the observers on the ziggurat. The planet Jupiter has a clear light and crosses Anu's way in a majestic orbit that most closely approximates an ellipse. It was therefore linked to Marduk, king of the gods, whose temper was terrible and whose power knew no bounds. It also became the planet of the Chaldean king, whose future destiny could be read in its course.

Finally, on the icy edges of the horizon shimmered Ninib, our pale, yellow planet Saturn, the farthest planet visible to the naked eye. Its slow progress along the zodiac, because of its distance from the earth, gave it the aspect of a morose old man. The Chaldeans believed that Ninib replaced the sun after the latter set, and called this ghostly substitute of the god Shamash "the sun of the night." That is why it, too, was thought to be powerful, despite its size; tempests and catastrophes were attributed to it.

Each celestial body ruled a plant, an animal species, a precious stone, and a color. Moreover, "certain actions, functions or professions, also each day and every hour, were integrated into the cycle of a divinity."[15]

The first astrological maxims we possess date back to 3000 B.C. The most famous ones are the predictions of Sargon the Old (2470–2430 B.C.). They are concerned almost entirely with presciences based on the appearance of the sun and the moon:

> "If the moon can be seen the first night of the month, the country will be peaceful; the heart of the country will rejoice. If the moon is surrounded with a halo, the King will reign supreme."

"If the setting sun seems twice as large as usual, and three of its rays are bluish, the King of the land is lost."

"If the moon is visible on the thirtieth, good tidings for the land of Akkad, bad for Syria."[16]

Gradually, these predictions became codified and divided into various sections. The Babylonian collection *Anu-Ea-Enlil,* for instance, has an entire section—called "Adad" from the name of the god of mountains—devoted to weather predictions:

"If a dark halo surrounds the moon, the month will be cloudy and rainy."

"If there is thunder in the month of Shebat, there will be a plague of locusts."

Other sections deal with foreign policy:

"If Mars is visible in the month of Tammuz (June–July), the warrior's bed will stay cold" (that is, there will be war).

"If Mercury is seen in the North, there will be many corpses; the King of Akkad will invade a foreign country."

Local politics were not forgotten:

"If Mars comes close to Gemini, a king will die and there will be rivalry."

Some predictions concerned the economy and the cost of living:

"If Jupiter seems to enter into the moon, prices will go down."[17]

As time went on, astrology continued to expand its influence. The kings themselves contributed to this development by asking the priests questions about the future of their country. We know some of the answers the royal astrologers gave, through the letters preserved on clay tables. Here is the prediction a certain Zâkir sent to King Sennacherib (letter #1214):

"In the month of Tammuz, the night of the tenth day, Scorpio will approach the moon. This is what it means: if Scorpio will be next to the right horn of the rising moon, the year will see the coming of a plague of locusts. They will destroy the harvest."[18]

Later the kings were not content with such impersonal forecasts. They and their chief dignitaries began to wish to lift the veils of fate for their own personal use.

The King's Future

Around the fifth century B.C. there appeared for the first time maxims that related a man's birthdate to his possible destiny. At first these predictions were obviously made only for the kings. The forecasts were based on the motion of the planets. Here are a few examples translated by Sachs:

"If a child is born when the moon has come forth, (then his life will be) bright, excellent, regular and long."
"If a child is born when Jupiter has come forth, (then his life will be) regular, well; he will become rich, he will grow old, (his) days will be long."
"If a child is born when Venus has come forth, (then his life will be) exceptionally calm; wherever he may go, it will be favorable; (his) days will be long."[19]

In general, the rising of heavenly bodies was considered favorable because then the positive characteristics of the gods were at their peak. By contrast, the setting of the same bodies was held to be a bad omen. The tablets that recorded the forecasts based on the setting of the planets have been lost, but we know the evil influence attributed to the setting from the previsions based on the motions of two planets at a time, one of which is on the way up, the other on the way down:

"If a child is born when Jupiter comes forth and Venus has set, it will go excellently with that man; his wife will leave and . . ." The rest of the fragment is missing, but its meaning is clear. We have seen that Jupiter represents the King. It rises when Venus, its bride, disappears over the horizon: "his wife will leave," that is, she will have to die before him.

The decline of Jupiter is a bad omen for the King: "If a child is born when Venus comes forth and Jupiter has set, his wife will be stronger than he." As she rises, Venus dominates her groom, Jupiter, who is disappearing in the darkness.

Some royal predictions based on the twelve signs of the zodiac have been found. We do not know any longer the exact circumstances under which these predictions were made, but they show some clear differences in the meaning that each sign had for human destiny:

"The place of Aries: death in his family,
The place of Taurus: death in battle,
The place of Gemini: death in prison . . ."

On the other hand:

"The place of Leo: he will grow old,
The place of Libra: good days . . ."[20]

Thus all was in order; the planets and the constellations each had seperate systems of influences.

The First Horoscopes

Slowly the desire to know their personal futures made people accept the belief that the sky at birth, with all its components, contained a summary of the god's intentions and that the relative position of the sun, the moon, and the planets at the date of birth or at conception could tell the course of each person's future. Thus horoscopes —which have had lasting impact up to our own days— owe their origins to the Babylonians. "The conclusion seems unavoidable," affirms Van der Waerden, "that horoscopic astronomy originated in Babylonia during the Persian reign."[21] In Babylonia the Persian rule began in 539 B.C.

The collection of Babylonian horoscopes that Sachs translated, dated between 409 and 141 B.C., is an unsurpassed source of documentation. These are not yet the horoscopes we know today, nor the ones the Greeks were familiar with. As Sachs writes, "No Babylonian horoscope mentions the Horoscopus (the computed zodiacal sign or point rising at the time of birth) or any of the secondary astrological positions which play important roles in Greco-Roman astrology."[22] Nevertheless, the essential structure is present. Here is one example of a horoscope published by Sachs. The birth to which it refers took place June 3, 234 B.C.:

> Year 77 of the Seleucid era, month Siman, from the 4th day, in the last part of the night of the 5th day, Aristokrates was born.
>
> That day: Moon in Leo. Sun in 12,30° in Gemini. The moon set its face from the middle toward the top; (there will ensue) destruction.
>
> Jupiter in 18° Sagittarius. The place of Jupiter means: (his life will be) regular, well; he will become rich, he will grow old, (his) days will be numerous.
>
> Venus in 4° Taurus. The place of Venus means: wherever he may go, it will be favorable (for him); he will have sons and daughters.

Mercury in Gemini, with the Sun. The place of Mercury means: the brave one will be first in rank, he will be more important than his brothers.

Saturn: 6° Cancer. Mars: 24° Cancer . . . (the rest of the predictions have been destroyed).[23]

As the history of horoscopes begins, that of Chaldean astrology, which started in the third millennium B.C. with predictions of the weather, of the success of crops, of the fate of the country as a whole, draws to a close. Later it involved foretelling the destiny of kings. With the conquest of Chaldea by the Greek warriors of Alexander the Great in 331 B.C., it advanced to the prediction of individual futures. This was the astrology the Greeks took over and transformed, through their unique genius, into a body of knowledge both elaborate and precise. They built astrology and horoscope-making into a form almost identical to that in which they are practiced today.

NOTES TO CHAPTER TWO

1. A. Koestler, *The Sleepwalkers* (New York: Macmillan, 1959).
2. M. Rutten, *La Science des Chaldéens* (Paris: P.U.F., 1960).
3. L. MacNeice, *Astrology* (London: Aldus Books, 1964).
4. Rutten, *op. cit.*
5. *Ibid.*
6. B. L. Van der Waerden, "History of the Zodiac," *Archiv für Orientforschung,* 216, 1953.
7. *Ibid.*
8. A. Sachs, "Babylonian Horoscopes," *Journal of Cuneiform Studies,* VI (1952), No. 2, 49.
9. Van der Waerden, *op. cit.*
10. W. Peuckert, *L'astrologie* (Paris: Payot, 1965).
11. A. Bouché-Leclercq, *L'astrologie grecque* (Paris: Leroux, 1899).
12. Peuckert, *op. cit.*
13. P. Courderc, *L'astrologie* (Paris: P.U.F., 1951).
14. Bouché-Leclercq, *op. cit.*
15. Rutten, *op cit.*
16. Lenormand, *Histoire ancienne des peuples de l'orient,* V, Paris.
17. Rutten, *op. cit.*
18. G. Conteneau, *La divination chez les Assyriens et les Babyloniens* (Paris: Payot, 1940).
19. Sachs, *op. cit.*
20. *Ibid.*
21. Van der Waerden, *op. cit.*
22. Sachs, *op. cit.*
23. *Ibid.*

From the Harmony of the Spheres to the Horoscope

IT WAS only about the ninth century B.C. that the Greeks learned to recognize the five planets. They named each one for its appearance, without reference to astrological notions. Homer, for instance, gave Venus two names: "Herald of the dawn" and "Vespertine," depending on whether it was seen in the morning or in the evening. The Greeks of this time did not yet realize that the two apparently distinct stars were in reality one and the same planet, sometimes preceding, sometimes following the progress of the sun. Mercury was known as "Twinkle Star," Mars as the "Fiery Star" because of its red color, Jupiter the "Luminous Star," and Saturn the "Brilliant Star."

The Greeks were not as patient observers as the Chaldeans had been. They distinguished constellations only vaguely and could barely tell the planets apart from the stars:

> Even the sun and the moon, although they were regarded as divinities like all the powers of nature,

occupied but a very secondary place in the Greek religion. Selene (the moon) does not appear to have obtained anywhere an organized cult, and in the few places where Helios (the sun) had temples, as for instance in the Island of Rhodes, a foreign origin may reasonably be suspected.[1]

By contrast the Greeks, much more than the Chaldeans, were interested in finding out the ultimate cause of things. Many thinkers began to represent the universe through mechanical models, abandoning earlier mythological explanations. Anaximander (610–547 B.C.), for instance, saw the earth as a cylinder surrounded by air, and the sun as nothing but the axle-hole of a gigantic wheel. Anaximene, who lived at the same time, thought that the stars were fixed like nails in a transparent crystal sphere rotating around the earth.

These ancient philosophers were followed, in the sixth century B.C., by Pythagoras of Samos. His famous theory on the "Harmony of the Spheres" stills holds a mysterious power over the depths of the unconscious. The Pythagorean universe was a sphere containing the earth and the air around it:

> Around it [the sphere] the sun, moon, and planets revolve in concentric circles, each fastened to a sphere or wheel. The swift revolution of each of these bodies causes a swish, or musical hum, in the air. Evidently each planet will hum on a different pitch, depending on the ratios of their respective orbits—just as the tone of a string depends on its length. Thus the orbits in which the planets move form a kind of huge lyre whose strings are curved into circles.[2]

Whether the harmony of the spheres is considered a poetic invention or a scientific concept, it introduced a religious element into the observation of the stars. In a later period Plato saw the sun and the stars, not as celestial bodies, but as gods. Aristotle also defended the notion of the divinity of stars, adding: "This world is inescapably linked to the motions of the world above. All power in this world is ruled by these motions."

The Influence of Berossus

The philosophers who believed in the divinity of the heavenly bodies did not ask the sky for glances at the future. Nevertheless, their new attitude toward the stars opened the way for popular beliefs in astrological divination. The connection of the immutable heavenly orbits with a divine origin was a heavy blow to the gods of traditional Greek mythology.

In the wake of Alexander's conquest of Chaldea in 331 B.C., the Greeks quickly abandoned their ancient mythological gods, protectors of the family and the city, in order to worship the heavens. The conquered Chaldeans imposed their astrological views on the conquering Greeks. Around 280 Berossus, priest of the Temple of Marduk in Babylon, moved to the Island of Cos, where Hippocrates, the creator of medicine, had taught two centuries earlier. Berossus grafted Chaldean astrology onto Hippocratic medicine. On Cos he wrote three long volumes in Greek, entitled *Babyloniaca*, in which he summarized the contents of both the clay tablets collected in the archives of his homeland and the annals of the ancient kings.

Berossus did not forget astrology. The school of Berossus had a great impact on Greek antiquity. Many scholars became disciples of the Chaldeans. Among these the most enthusiastic were the Stoics. It was mostly due to their influence that astrology was later adopted by the Romans, too. In fact, as the historian Franz Cumont has said,

> Stoicism conceived the world as a great organism, the "sympathetic" forces of which acted and re-acted necessarily upon one another, and was bound in consequence to attribute a predominating influence to the celestial bodies, the greatest and the most powerful of all in nature, and Destiny, connected with the infinite succession of causes, readily agreed also with the determinism of the Chaldeans, founded, as it was, upon the regularity of the sidereal movements.[3]

Babylon, destroyed again by a fire in 125 B.C., disappeared from history. But before dying it planted the seed of astrology deep into Greek soil. With their individualism, their curiosity for all new ideas, their penchant for subtle reasoning, the Greeks were not content just to borrow Chaldean astrology without changing it. In response to pressures from a populace whose members wanted to know their personal fortunes, astrology in Greece became an infinitely complex lore.

Astrology In Rome

But the wheels of fate keep turning. Only two centuries after having conquered the world, Greece in its turn was defeated and occupied by the Roman legions. The torch of astrology was now passed to the Romans, just as it had been received earlier from the vanquished Babylonians. The history of astrology in Rome is well known to us through the works of Bouché-Leclercq and Fr. H. Cramer.

It was through slaves of Greek origin that astrology first infiltrated Rome. These were mostly charlatans without any real knowledge, predicting anything for anyone. At first their success was confined to the lower classes; the educated citizens looked down on their activities. They were called derisively "astrologers of the circus," since most of their income came from predicting winners at the chariot races, on which the Romans liked to bet heavily. But soon the traditional diviners of Rome, the augurs, began to feel threatened by the newcomers. They took umbrage and reacted swiftly. A decree of Cornelius Hispallus expelled from the city "these Chaldeans who exploit the people under the false pretense of reading the stars."[4] The decree went on to state that astrology was an untruthful means of prediction, but this opposition only helped to strengthen the popularity of the astrologers.

Under the Roman Republic (200 B.C.–44 B.C.), the citizens were slowly converted to astrology, mostly because of the involvement of the intellectuals. The philosophers began to argue about it. Some, like the Stoics, who thought that men were toys in the hands of fate, defended astrology. Others, led by the Greek Carneades, opposed it on the grounds that man possesses free will.

After 139 B.C., Rome entered the troubled period that was eventually to end with the fall of the Republic. The period was very favorable to astrology. The consuls Marius and Octavius, and later Julius Caesar and Pompey, had their horoscopes prepared in great detail. Yet there were still a few great men who were unrelenting in their opposition to astrology. Lucretius, and of course Cicero, remained the last great skeptics. In his *On Divinations,* Cicero uses every valid argument against this superstition. However, a comet that appeared sometime after the death of Julius Caesar was enough to brush all his objections aside.

During the Empire, almost every emperor had his personal astrologer. In *Astrology in Roman Law and Politics,* Fr. H. Cramer devotes special attention to "the dynasty of imperial astrologers of the first century of our era,"[5] and to their influence on important political decisions. Emperor Augustus had his destiny interpreted according to the horoscope of both his birth and his conception; to have both was the height of refinement in his age. His court astrologer, Thrasyllus, became the adviser of Tiberius, his successor. It is said that Thrasyllus' task was to prepare the horoscopes of all the ambitious people at the emperor's court and to reveal to him the names of the ones the stars seemed to favor for the imperial throne. Tiberius had all of them executed, to avoid any potential competition. Balbillus, Thrasyllus' son, was the astrologer of Emperor Claudius, then of Nero. It has been said that the emperor Domitian used astrology the same way Tiberius did. And Septimius Severus allegedly married a woman whose horoscope had predicted that she would marry a future emperor.

The Fall of the Roman Empire

In the period of decadence, every poet seemed to pride himself on his faith—or even accomplishments—in astrology. Bouché-Leclercq has given us a vivid description of this astrological fad in literature:

> Under the rule of Augustus, astrology was decidedly fashionable. Everybody pretended to have a smattering of the lore, and writers multiplied allusions which they knew could be understood by worldly readers. Never had the stars had such a place in literature. . . . The ancient epic diviners, Melampus, Tiresias, Chalcas, Helenus, were celebrated more than ever, and they were attributed a knowledge of "the science of stars"

commensurate with current requirements. . . . . Virgil,
unskilled at flattery, proposed to rename Libra after
Augustus, the reigning emperor (since he was as just
and equitable "as that sign of the zodiac"). Lucan would
have put Nero in place of the sun. . . ."[6]

The astrological fever did not spare women. Juvenal
in his *Satires* makes fun of the frivolous women of high
society who did nothing without consulting their horoscopes. He advises them against this practice:

> Beware the Woman too, and shun her Sight,
> Who, in these Studies, does her self Delight.
> By whom a greasie Almanack is born,
> with often handling, like chaste Amber, worn:
> Not now consulting, but consulted, she
> of the Twelve Houses, and their Lords, is free,
> She, if the Scheme a fatal Journey show,
> stays safe at Home, but lets her Husband go.
> If but a Mile she Travel out of Town,
> the Planetary House must first be known:
> And luck moment; if her Eye but akes
> or itches, its Decumbiture she takes.
> No Nourishment receives in her Disease,
> but what the Stars, and Ptolemy shall please.[7]

From the fourth century onward, everyone in Rome
believed in astrology. "A certain faith in astrology was
part of common sense, and only excessive trust was
thought to be superstitious."[8] With the fall of the Empire, Cramer writes, came "the twilight of 'scientific' astrology and the rise of star worship."[9] Superstition and
debauchery reached their zenith in the reign of blood-
thirsty Heliogabalus. This emperor attempted to reestab-
lish the cult of Helios, the sun. As his name indicates,
he pretended to be its living incarnation. But the attempt had no success; the disorganized and weakened

Empire was soon to disappear under the barbarian waves pouring in from the north and the east.

A great voice was raised amid this decaying antiquity: that of Saint Augustine, bishop of Hippo in North Africa, who lived from 354 to 430 A.D. In his *Confessions* he tries to show the danger and falsity of divination by the stars:

> The astrologers say: "it is from the heavens that the irresistible cause of sin comes, it is due to the conjunction of Venus with Mars or Saturn." Thus man is absolved of all faults, he who is only proudly rotting flesh. The blame is indeed given to the creator and ruler of the heavens and of the stars.[10]

The disappearance of the Roman Empire signaled the triumph of Christian faith over the faith of astrology.

An Astonishing Codification

What happened to astrological doctrine during this period? With the Greeks and the Romans, astrology acquired its "classic" outlines. In the long centuries that followed, no essential feature was added or subtracted. The astrological arsenal of the Greeks was a systematic code of alleged influences, a language of infinite resources. The forecast of an astrologer today seems almost identical with one a Greek or Roman astrologer could have given two thousand years ago.

In their book, *Greek Horoscopes*,[11] the historian Neugebauer and Van Hoesen, Director of Brown University Library, have published 180 Greek birth themes that have come down to our days. These fragments were written originally between 70 B.C. and 600 A.D. Most of them are dated around 100 A.D., indicating the considerable development of horoscopy in that period. The two authors have amply commented on these astrological themes, which pinpoint heavenly positions much more accurately than the Chaldeans' did. Moreover, they take into account the precise hour of birth. The Greek word *horoscopos* literally means: "I watch that which is rising." Originally the word was not used to refer to the whole planetary pattern at the moment of birth, as it is today, but only to the point of the zodiac rising over the horizon at the exact moment of birth. The idea is that, at birth, the infant is submitted to the influence of the constellation that is also being born. This "horoscope" point is just an abstract segment of the skies, yet it assumes a basic importance, since the whole orientation of the future depends on it. The child is seen as a sensitive photographic plate. At the very instant in which he gives forth his first cry, all the astrological influences converge on his cradle and blend together to develop his destiny.

The First Astrological Treatises

To extend our acquaintance with the meaning of astral influences, we can consult some of the volumes on astrology written at the beginning of the Christian age. They are more detailed and accurate than the ambiguous ancient horoscopes. The *Astronomicon* of the Roman author Manilius is the oldest known treatise on astrology.[12] It was composed during the reign of Caesar Augustus, around 10 A.D. The book is written in verse; there are 4,200 verses, divided into five books. It refers back constantly to the Greek astrologers and to their predecessors on the banks of the Nile and the Euphrates. It is, then, first of all a compilation of previously known lore, and it is as such that it is extremely important to us. An

even better known work is the *Tetrabiblos* by Ptolemy
of Alexandria, written in 140 A.D.[13] Ptolemy was indis-
putably one of the greatest astronomers of antiquity; the
world system that bears his name had the earth as the
center of the universe and assumed a theory of epicycles
to explain the visible planetary movements. The system
was accepted by astronomers the world over until the
days of Copernicus and Kepler. The *Tetrabiblos* of
Ptolemy completed Manilius' *Astronomicon* without
contradicting it.

A careful study of these two works shows that Greek
astrology took over all the elements that the Chaldeans
had already well standardized. "Most names of Greek
zodiacal signs are translations or small modifications of
the Babylonian names," writes Van der Waerden.[14]
With the planets a sort of naturalization took place, by
which the Chaldean gods were assimilated into Olympus. Nebo, Ishtar, Nergal, Marduk, and Ninib became
Hermes, Aphrodite, Ares, Zeus, and Kronos. Franz Cumont remarks, "The names of the planets which we em-
ploy today are an English translation of a Latin translation of a Greek translation of a Babylonian nomenclature."[15] But the signs of the zodiac and the seven stars
of the solar system acquired a variety of meanings infinitely more complex, more individual, with the Greeks
than they had with the Chaldeans. Here is how Ptolemy
in the *Tetrabiblos* describes the physical appearance of
people born under Saturn:

> First, among the planets, Saturn, if he is in the orient,
> makes his subjects in appearance dark-skinned, robust,
> black-haired, curly-haired, hairy-chested, with eyes of
> moderate size, of middling stature, and in tempera-
> ment having an excess of the moist and cold. If Saturn
> is setting, in appearance he makes them dark, slender,

small, straight-haired, with little hair on the body, rather graceful, and black-eyed; in temperament, sharing most in the cold and dry. (Book III, 11)[16]

Later the brides of those born under the influence of Saturn are described: "He makes the wives hard-working and stern"; followed by the husband: "If Saturn is similarly in aspect with the sun, they marry sedate, useful, industrious husbands." (Book IV, 5)

The influence of the planet is blended with that of the sign it crosses at the time of birth. Manilius explains in his astrological poem:

> No sign nor planet serves itself alone,
> Each blends the other's virtues with its own,
> Mixing their force, and interchanged they reign,
> Signs planets bound, and planets signs again.[17]

For example, when Mars crosses the sign of Aries, it promises the most in warlike virtues, because they "match well." On the other hand, most of its virtues are lost in crossing Cancer, a dreamlike sign under the moon's domain.

In the *Astronomicon* the concept of the "zodiacal man" is clearly mentioned for the first time. Each sign is thought to correspond to a part of the human body. Here is a racy seventeenth-century translation of verses 698 to 706 of Book IV by Manilius:

> The Ram defends the Head, the Neck the Bull,
> The Arms, bright Twins, are subject to your Rule:
> I'th' Shoulders Leo, and the Crab's obeyed
> I'th' Breast, and in the Guts the modest Maid:
> I'th' Buttocks Libra, Scorpio warms Desires
> in Secret Parts, and spreads unruly Fires:
> The Thighs the Centaur, and the Goat commands
> the Knees, and binds them up with double bands.

The parted Legs in moist Aquarius meet,
And Pisces gives Protection to the Feet.[18]

Greek and Roman Innovations

Every astronomical discovery helped to extend the domain of astrology. There was no measurable space in the skies without its astrological interpretation. Thus it was with the aspects between planets, that is, their relative position on the celestial sphere. This contribution was a typically Greek idea: "The polygonal aspects, of which there is no trace in Chaldean documents, dominate the theory and practice of Greek astrology. This is a kind of heavenly ballistics that consists in the planets' sending each other rays that can be either favorable or evil."[19]

This is how it worked: The planets do not move with the same speed across the sky. They seem to come together, to pass and overtake each other, assuming different angular positions in regard to each other as seen by an observer on earth. The Greek astronomers attached a particular importance to the distance between bodies in the solar system that happened to be at the apex of simple geometrical figures: the triangle, the square, and the hexagon. Pythagoras' theory of the harmony of spheres had much to do with this new concern. When two celestial bodies are 180 degrees apart at the moment of their appearance on the horizon, this is called an opposition. The forecast drawn from an opposition is unfavorable because the influences of the two celestial bodies contradict each other.

The astrologers went on to divide the heavenly sphere into twelve equal sections, which they called houses:

> To give more meaning to the place that a planet occupies in the sky, the apparent daily movement of

the sun around the earth each twenty-four hours was taken by the Greek astrologers to be analogous with the sun's apparent yearly journey. This meant a kind of a year 365 times shorter than a regular one. By such peculiar reasoning they obtained an analogy of the sun's passage through the year with its passage through the day. [The astrologers divided the] astrological day into twelve parts, in the pattern of the twelve signs of the zodiac. Each day the sun passes through the twelve houses 365 times faster than it passes through the signs of the zodiac. The planets, which travel through the whole zodiac just as the sun does, cross the twelve astrological houses within twenty-four hours, too, but each at a different hour.[20]

In his astrological poem, Manilius describes the meanings of these twelve astrological houses extensively. His descriptions can be found without any changes in today's astrological manuals. They are based on analogies of the planetary positions during their daily course. Thus Manilius derives the meaning of the fourth house from its position directly underneath the earth, at the lowest point of the daily astral round:

> In the nether part of the sky, at the lower pivot of the world from which the whole circle can be seen above, this house is situated in the middle of the night. Saturn, whose rule over the gods was overthrown, who lost the throne of the universe, exercises his power in those depths. As a father he influences the fate of fathers, and the destiny of the aged is also under his control (*Astronomicon*, Book II).[21]

Even today, according to astrologers, it is the fourth house that rules the relatives of a newborn and the end of its life. Among the Greek horoscopes translated by Neugebauer and Von Hoesen, almost all the ones dated after the Christian age include this division into astrological houses.

The various innovations that the Greeks and the Romans progressively added to astrology would take hundreds of pages to enumerate. It is beyond our purpose to do so here; it will be sufficient to quote a few examples.

The Greek astrologers attempted to date the main events of a life, happy or unhappy. They made the horoscope into an almost living thing, which passed through lucky and unlucky times. To achieve this they assumed that the points of the zodiac occupied by the planets at an infant's birth remained sensitive to the end of its life. The planetary motions regularly returned the orbs to these sensitive points of the zodiac, thereby precipitating favorable or nefarious events for the subject. These were called planetary transits. It was believed that the exact date of such future events could be accurately predicted, since the astrologers were able to compute the position of planets some time in advance.

There were other techniques used to establish precisely the limits of a man's destiny. Thus the primary directions, secondary directions, and solar revolutions were developed to help project the birth horoscope into the future. Soon it was decided to add or subtract the longitude of a planet to or from that of another, in order to get imaginary points called parts—the part of fortune, of friends, of money, of death, etc.—these were inscribed along the rim of the horoscopic circle to help in the prediction.

The Blind Alley of Astrology

The superficial logic of all these systems was unfortunately nothing but superstition under a thin coat of mathematics. A.J. Festugière, the historian, writes in this context: "Hellenistic astrology is a mixture of a seductive philosophical doctrine, an absurd mythology, and inconsistently applied methods."[22] The harshness of this judgment is quite appropriate. The Greeks did run into a blind alley in their attempt to establish scientific laws relating the cosmos to human life. Their admirable philosophy, the speculations of their astronomers, the discoveries of their mathematicians were finally unable to unveil the mystery of astral influences.

And yet, like the Chaldeans, the Greeks also felt, vaguely but justly, that man is constantly influenced by the cosmic forces that surround him. Perhaps a few even glimpsed some truths. But the Greeks' desire to unravel their own personal destinies was too strong and prevented them from formulating the questions correctly. It is certainly plausible, however, that the state of their knowledge made such a task impossible in their age under the best conditions.

Whatever the cause, this failure had a dramatic impact on the history of ideas. It promoted a popular belief in the stars bolstered by the prestige of the great Greek classics. This belief has led, in our days, to the foolish fortune-telling we are all too familiar with. But in between there was one brilliant interlude.

NOTES TO CHAPTER THREE

1. F. Cumont, *Astrology and Religion Among the Greeks and Romans* (New York: Dover, 1960).
2. A. Koestler, *The Sleepwalkers* (New York: Macmillan, 1959).
3. Cumont, *op. cit.*
4. P. Couderc, *L'astrologie* (Paris: P.U.F., 1951).
5. Fr. H. Cramer, *Astrology in Roman Law and Politics* (Philadelphia: The American Philosophical Society, 1954).
6. A. Bouché-Leclercq, *L'astrologie grecque* (Paris: Leroux, 1899).
7. Juvenal, *The Sixth Satire*, translated by John Dryden, 1693.
8. Bouché-Leclercq, *op. cit.*
9. Cramer, *op. cit.*
10. Saint Augustine, *Confessions*, IV, 3.
11. O. Neugebauer and H. B. Van Hoesen, *Greek Horoscopes* (Philadelphia: The American Philosophical Society, 1959).
12. Manilius, *Astronomicon*, translated in the eighteenth century.
13. C. Ptolemy, *Tetrabiblos*, translated by W.G. Waddels and F.E. Robbins (Cambridge: Harvard University Press, 1956).
14. B. L. Van der Waerden, "History of the Zodiac," *Archiv für Orientforschung*, 216, 1953.
15. Cumont, *op. cit.*
16. Ptolemy, *op. cit.*
17. Manilius, *op. cit.*
18. *Ibid.*
19. Bouché-Leclercq, *op. cit.*
20. M. Gauquelin, *L'astrologie devant la science* (Paris: Planéte, 1965).
21. Manilius, *op. cit.*
22. A. J. Festugière, *La Révélation d'Hermes Trismegiste* (Paris: Gabalda, 1950).

A Brilliant Interlude

IN EUROPE, astrology assumed a new aspect in the fifteenth and sixteenth centuries, along with the arts and sciences. The Western world discovered the existence of the classic texts of antiquity the Arabs had preserved. These brought on an immediate and widespread interest in everything Greek and Roman.

It has been said often and correctly that the Renaissance marked the beginning of modern science. But the Renaissance was also, more than any other period, an age of paradoxes. It was in this age, after all, that all the ancient occult sciences triumphed. This intellectual inconsistency may surprise the modern scientist, but it did not seem to upset the great men of the Renaissance. They all shared a powerful interest in the exact sciences with a taste for the superstitious doctrines of the past. Or was it really a taste for superstition? Could they have hoped, with some reason, to discover by means of occultism an ancient wisdom lost through the centuries, one full of promise for the future?

The fact is that classical astrology fascinated Renaissance scholars. They did not content themselves with collecting its findings without changes; they tried to integrate the great discoveries of their time with the mystery of astral influences. There is no better example of this paradoxical tension than in the great creative genius of Kepler.

Kepler and Astrology

Johannes Kepler was born in Weil (Wurttemberg) on December 27, 1571, at 2:30 P.M., "after a pregnancy of 224 days, 9 hours, and 53 minutes," as he writes. Such precision on Kepler's part is only one indication of his interest in astrology. It would not be an exaggeration to say that his belief in the occult contributed strongly to making him one of the founders of modern astronomy. He devoted all his life to proving the Pythagorean thesis of the harmony of the spheres, according to which each planet sounds in its orbit a different musical note. It was this obsession, joined to a boundless perseverance and a mathematical genius, that enabled him to succeed in formulating the laws of planetary motions that made him famous.

Although various princes supported Kepler all through his adventurous life, he was constantly pressured into predicting the future for the astrological almanacs, just as the other court astronomers of the period were. He hated making these predictions, which he denounced as "horrible superstitions" and "monkey-business."[1] One day he confessed: "Like a stubborn mule, a mind trained in mathematic deductions will resist for a long time when confronted with the erroneous foundations of astrology; only a hail of curses and blows will force it to step in that mire."[2]

Yet he wrote several treatises on astrology and even developed a theory to account for planetary influences. What was Kepler's real opinion? According to Arthur

Koestler, he "believed in the possibility of a new and true astrology as an exact empirical science."[3] One of Kepler's works, the *Tertius Interveniens,* carries the following inscription for a motto: "A warning to certain theologians, physicists, and philosophers ... who, while rightly rejecting the superstitions of the astrologers, ought not to throw out the baby with the bath water."[4] "Because," as he wrote in the same book, "it should not seem incredible that from the stupidities and blasphemies of the astrologers a new, healthy and useful learning may arise." In a letter he wrote on October 2, 1606, to Harriot, an astrologer friend of his, it is clear that he rejected the major part of the old beliefs:

> I hear you had troubles because of your astrology. Do you think it is worth it? It is ten years now since I rejected the divisions into twelve equal parts, into houses; into dominations, trinities, and so forth. The only part I kept are the aspects, and I link astrology to the doctrine of harmonies.[5]

Thus Kepler had faith in astrology, even if a limited one: "Everything that is or that happens in the visible sky is felt in some hidden fashion by earth and nature"—as he writes in *De Stella Nova.*[6]

A Paradoxical Way of Thinking

The profound dilemma that haunted Kepler's conscience also haunted every great man of his age. Freedom of thought allowed them a conception of astronomical models at variance with the one that had been held for over fifteen hundred years and that had been accepted and codified by the Christian religion.

Was the earth really at the center of the universe? The

question was answered negatively by Copernicus (1473–1543) in the famous work published the year of his death, *De Revolutionibus Orbium Caelestium*. There Copernicus resurrected the forgotten insight of Aristarchus of Samos (third century B.C.) and placed the sun at the center of the universe, while the earth was only one among the planets revolving around the sun.

It has often been said that this discovery sounded the knell for astrology, since the earth could no longer be the focus of all planetary influences. This distinction would now belong to the new center, the sun. Yet Copernicus was not an opponent of astrology. Although he never prepared horoscopes himself, he accepted the help of Rheticus, a well-known astrologer, in the preparation of the first edition of his masterpiece.

One notices the same attitude in the Italian Geronimo Cardano (1501–1576). Cardano was a physician, a mathematician, a philosopher, and an astrologer. He published a voluminous astronomical treatise, *Genitarum Exempla,* in which a number of famous horoscopes were collected. This did not, however, prevent him from simultaneously contributing several useful discoveries to algebra or from teaching mathematics in Milan. He also invented the ingenious suspension device that permits navigators to stabilize a compass despite the movements of a ship.

We meet the same paradox in the character of the Swiss physician Paracelsus (1493–1541). Paracelsus formulated a theory by which all contemporary medicine, astrology, and alchemy were reconciled in surprising harmony. The basic postulate for this theory was a correspondence between the external world, especially the heavens, and the various parts of the interior world, that is, the human organism. A universal principle, which he called *magnale magnum,* ruled over everything by virtue of a kind of cosmic magnetism. Consequently, he claimed that a doctor should always consult the skies before writing his prescriptions. The seven major organs of the human body corresponded to the seven planets. The operation of the heart was governed by the sun, that of the lungs by Saturn, the brains by the moon, Venus ruled over the kidneys, Jupiter over the liver, and Mars over the black bile. This strange theory had the great merit of opening the way to the doctrine of specific cure and chemical therapy.

In the next century Newton (1642–1727) was just as receptive to astrology as he was to other forms of occultism. Yet it was he who discovered the laws of universal gravitation, which replaced the old astrological theory of planetary forces. At the same time he would mention that his reason for attending Cambridge University was "to find out what was true in astrology." It is also recorded "that when the astronomer Halley, of comet fame, made a slighting remark as to the value of astrology, Newton gently rebuked him thus: 'I have studied the subject, Mr. Halley; you have not.' "[7]

In fact, astrology was to retain its official status in Europe up to the end of the seventeenth century. In France, Morin de Villefranche (1583–1656) was one of the last great astrologers paid by the State. He finished his career as professor of mathematics at the Collège de France, after having compiled *Astrologia Gallica,* a work of twenty-six volumes. Although this collection of lore was unoriginal, it exercised a great deal of influence over contemporary astrologers. Morin de Villefranche died honored and respected.

Nevertheless, ten years after his death, Colbert, the minister of Louis XIV, concurrently with the foundation of the Academy of Sciences, obtained a ban con-

demning astrology, which thereafter disappeared forever
from France's official sphere. The same pattern was repeated in short order in other West European nations.

Astrological Almanacs

Astrology, however, did not disappear. It lived on in
the imagination of poets. Thus Goethe began his autobiography with these words:

> On the 28th of August 1749, at midday, as the clock
> struck twelve, I came into the world, at Frankfort-on-
> the-Main. The aspect of the stars was propitious: The
> sun stood in the sign of the Virgin, and had culminated
> for the day; Jupiter and Venus looked on with a
> friendly eye, and Mercury not adversely; the attitude
> of Saturn and Mars was neutral; the Moon alone, just
> full, exerted all the more her power of opposition as
> she had just reached her planetary hour. She, there-
> fore, resisted my birth which could not be accomplished
> until this hour was passed. These auspicious aspects
> which the astrologers subsequently interpreted very
> favourably for me, may have been the causes of my
> preservation.[8]

But from the eighteenth century on, there were fewer
and fewer informed men who believed in astrology. Its
popularity survived instead in the countryside, by means
of astrological almanacs that were passed around from
village to village. These almanacs maintained the primitive tradition the Chaldean astrologers had originated,
binding together astral influences with the weather, plant
growth, and animal and human life. Their influence in
the countryside was considerable from the Middle Ages
up to the beginning of the twentieth century. The influence of almanacs began to wane only as the progress of

meteorology and medicine started to affect the rural populations. They finally disappeared when they were replaced by radio or television sets.

The almanacs, which contained an astonishing brew of religious prayers and beliefs in all sorts of influences, were filled with a variety of suggestions: precepts for saving one's soul, advice for the health of men and livestock, and weather forecasts for farmers. Probably the most popular almanac was *The Great Calendar and Shepherd's Guide,* first printed in 1491. In this work are compiled, helter-skelter, a listing of the divisions of the year, the months, religious holidays, religious advice, astrological predictions, a description of the sufferings of the damned in Hell, and, above all, "a little treatise to find out under which planet the infant was born, as well as the character of the twelve signs of the zodiac." This book was a bible for a dozen generations.

Thus in both rural and urban areas there remained a powerful astrologico-medical tradition for the use of the masses. "The barber-surgeon letting blood had no medical training whatsoever. But he had to have at least a smattering of astrology. In some towns, the regulations prescribed that bleeding was allowed only when 'the moon was right.' "[9]

Medicinal plants derived their virtues by association with certain planets. Nicholas Culpeper, in his *The English Physician Enlarged* of 1653, devoted a chapter to "The Stars' Own Vegetable Garden and Medicine Chest." Among various other things, it related that Jupiter rules "the oak and the orange, peas and dandelion" and that Mars is responsible for "onion, mustard, radish, peppers." As a remedy for intellectual fatigue, for example, Culpeper recommended the "lily of the valley, for it is under the dominion of Mercury, and therefore it strengthens the brain, recruiting a weak memory, and makes it strong again."[10]

The Blind Alley of the Renaissance

We have seen the crude utilitarianism that corrupted the metaphysical questioning of the great Renaissance geniuses, those original and independent minds who built the modern world. Kepler's intuitions and the efforts of Paracelsus ended in childishly naive representations of a magic world long rejected by science. Thus the attempts of the Renaissance to sound the mystery of astral influences resulted in one more failure.

There is no doubt that several Renaissance scholars did sense the possibility of a new science of astral influence, as the Greeks had earlier. But, failing to find the key to the problem, failing to formulate questions in verifiable terms, they gave in to the lure of all metaphysical systems: to substitute myths for an empirical science.

At the dawn of the twentieth century astrology, abandoned by scholars, remained a dark maze through which Kepler and Newton had once walked full of hope. The brilliant interlude of the Renaissance had proved barren as far as the knowledge of astral influences was concerned. At least one could have hoped that mankind would have learned the uselessness of looking to the planetary motions for a resolution of its daily problems. Unfortunately, this has not happened either. In the twentieth century, against all expectations, belief in horoscopes has flared up stronger than ever.

NOTES TO CHAPTER FOUR

1. J. Kepler, *Tertius Interveniens*, G. W., VI, 145 ff.
2. ———, *De Stella Nova in Pede Serpentarii*, G. W., I, 147 ff.
3. A. Koestler, *The Sleepwalkers* (New York: Macmillan, 1959).
4. Kepler, *Tertius Interveniens, op. cit.*
5. W. Peuckert, *L'astrologie* (Paris: Payot, 1965).
6. Kepler, *De Stella Nova in Pede Serpentarii, op. cit.*
7. M. Palmer Hall, *The Story of Astrology* (Philadelphia: David McKay, 1943).
8. J. W. von Goethe, *Autobiography* (Washington: Public Affairs Press, 1949).
9. P. Saintyves, *L'astrologie populaire, et l'influence de la lune* (Paris: Nourry, 1937).
10. L. MacNeice, *Astrology* (London: Aldus Books, 1964).

Astral Psychoanalysis

D R. HANS BENDER, Professor of Psychology at the University of Freiburg in Germany, writes, in the introduction to a sociological study on astrology:

> It is striking that more than three hundred years of experimental sciences have not succeeded in providing an antidote to astrological beliefs. Astrology is a social reality. Its forms vary from the crudest superstitions to thoughtful attempts at connecting the astrologer's magic vision of the world with modern psychological knowledge. . . . Therefore astrology poses a problem of social and psychological health.[1]

The Twentieth Century

The rebirth of astrology began between the two wars. At first it showed up in the United States, Canada, and England; later it spread to continental Europe.

Astrology has benefited from the powerful communications media the modern world has at its disposal. Today astrology is everywhere. The belief has spread out over the planet like a universal language, a kind of Esperanto for telling the future. Innumerable dollars, francs, lire, and marks change hands every day because of it. Thousands of people plan their actions in conformity with astrological directives. Yet no great addition has been made to the doctrines already condemned by the academies. The weightiest change was the totally gratuitous inclusion of the supposed influences of the newly discovered planets, Uranus, Neptune, and Pluto.

But the success of horoscopes goes on. According to Louis MacNeice,

> It has been estimated that in the U.S.A. there are over 5,000 working astrologers, who cater for about 10,000,000 customers. The charge in America for an individual horoscope can often get as high as £100; in Britain the average fee is about £10, though it can be as low as £2 or as high as £50. Their clients come from all walks of life: from young girls in search of romance to politicians and financiers. Thus there is little doubt that astrology today is very much alive (perhaps more alive than ever before). . . . Newspaper horoscopes are astrology's most obvious medium in the modern world. Almost every major popular newspaper in America and Britain features an astrological column, as do many big newspapers in Europe. . . . And, apart from the large numbers of magazines devoted exclusively to astrology (in the U.S.A. the most popular, *Horoscope*, has a monthly circulation of 170,000), there are innumerable periodicals that run a regular horoscope feature. These are usually women's magazines, though evidence shows that men read them too.[2]

In India the whole back page of the daily papers is devoted to astrology. Parents list short summaries of their marriageable children's horoscopes, hoping to attract a good match by listing the qualities of their offspring.

In the Orient an important marriage cannot take place

without the astrologer's advice. In Japan, *Life* wrote in 1960, "Japanese publishers last year sold eight million copies of horoscope pamphlets called koyomi.[3]

Several countries have astrological societies that offer regular courses, followed by a general examination, and deliver diplomas as recognized universities do. The *American Federation of Astrologers* in the U.S. grants a "Certificate of Proficiency after successfully passing the Professional Examination in Natal Astrology." In England, the Faculty of Astrological Studies gives a diploma that allows its holder to add *D.F.Astrol.S.* after his name.

Nostradamus and the Nazis

The late success of the prophecies of Nostradamus (1503–1566) is a clear symptom of the rebirth of astrology. It is now over four hundred years since Michel de Nostredame, known as Nostradamus, brought out his famous *Centuries,* in which he presumed to reveal the future of the world. Edgar Leoni, in *Nostradamus: Life and Literature,*[4] has recently published a complete study of the main subsequent interpretations given to the *Centuries.* His work indicates that in every succeeding century there have been analysts who imagined they perceived in Nostradamus' jargon the explanation for the most minute events of their own times. On this score we are keeping up with the past.

It has been said that in World War II the Nazis formed a monstrous alliance with astrology. A study by E. Howe goes a long way toward separating the truth from the myth on this issue.[5] One fact is certain: during the war Hitler's court attached a great importance to the prophecies of Nostradamus. Goebbels, the propaganda minister, employed several astrologers whose task was to bring out a pro-German edition of the *Centuries* to be distributed among enemy populations. Among these editors was Karl Ernst Krafft, one of the best known astrologers of those days. Rudolph Hess, Hitler's heir apparent and most trusted counsellor, was the main patron of astrologers. After Hess's flight to Scotland in 1941, Hitler's rage against him was reflected on the diviners, many of whom were sent to concentration camps. Krafft, who was not able to foresee this turn of events, died in a concentration camp on January 8, 1945. According to one Louis de Wohl, the Allies in turn were helped by his astrological knowledge to prepare their own versions of prophecies by Nostradamus for use as propaganda against the Germans. But according to the historian E. Howe, there is slight chance that this is true.

Astrology has always been helped by periods of trouble, but the return of peace has not ended its ascendancy. The famous psychoanalyst C. G. Jung recognized the strength of the belief in the stars when he wrote: "Today out of the social deeps, it knocks at the doors of the universities from which it was banished some three hundred years ago."[6]

As the first interplanetary journeys are about to begin, men of science are finding in this belief a grave and paradoxical symptom. During the last dozen years a number of them have decided to reevaluate the problems of astrology by means of the intellectual equipment of modern science. The curtain is now rising on the second act, which promises to be as short as the first one was long. During the first act astrology reigned supreme; in the second it will have to meet modern science face to face.

Sociological Studies

The social problem presented by astrology has seemed important enough to professional sociologists for them to devote several studies to it. Who are the people who believe in astrology? Why do they believe in it? In 1963, the French Public Opinion Institute published the results of research into the attitudes of the adult population regarding astrology. Here are the main conclusions of the study:[7]

Fifty-eight per cent of the population know their birth signs.

Thirty-eight per cent have at one time or another wished to have a personal horoscope made.

Fifty-three per cent of the people regularly read their horoscopes in the papers.

These high percentages are understandable in light of the very favorable opinions held about astrology:

Forty-three per cent believe that astrologers are scientists.

Thirty-seven per cent believe that there is a relationship between the character of persons and the sign under which they were born.

Twenty-three per cent believe that predictions come true.

Of course, astrology and astronomy are often thought to be synonymous. Every day, in fact, astronomical observatories get requests for horoscopes.

The results of the inquiry have also been broken down according to the respondents' social class. Belief in astrology does not seem to be influenced by either income or level of education. Farmers are somewhat immune to the charms of astrology, while those in the liberal professions respond more readily—especially artists and financiers. This supports the reputation of Hollywood and Wall Street as strongholds of astrology.

Finally, the results were used to draw a "profile" of the typical astrologer's customer. She is a young woman between twenty-five and thirty, of good education and above-average income. She is mainly interested in her personal future, but is also concerned with predictions about world politics. Other people's futures are of little interest to her.

The German Institute of Demoscopy has also conducted a very detailed study, based on over 10,000 interviews, between the years 1952 and 1956.[8] Here are some of the more important findings:

The question "Do you believe that there is a connection between the destiny of men and the stars?" was answered in the affirmative by 30 per cent of the sample, and 20 per cent more said that they thought it was possible. Among those who believed in astrology, more than half (56 per cent) thought that astrological columnists were trained people capable of accurate prediction.

The German study also showed the extraordinary popularity of the zodiacal signs: 69 per cent of those interviewed knew the sign of their birth.

Moreover, 15 per cent of those who believed in astrology claimed that with its help politics could be conducted more efficiently. Finally, 7 per cent of those who sympathized with astrology had their personal horoscopes made at one time or another. This proportion may seem fairly low; however, as Dr. G. Schmidtchen notes, it means that two million Germans have had their own horoscopes drawn up, and if the ratio holds, American astrologers have at least six million faithful customers.

Astrological Archetypes

According to Jung, astrology is deeply rooted in the human soul. The sight of the starry firmament has always made men dream, and these heavenly dreams, accumulated over thousands and thousands of years all over the world, have left a residue in the consciousness of the race. These are the archetypes. The psychological sketches that astrologers have been outlining for the past two thousand years are a simplified version of modern psychodiagnostics. Let us listen, for example, to what an astrologer says about the sign of Capricorn:

> Governed by Saturn. Closed, reserved, sober, disciplined, calm, thoughtful, patient, cold, detached, ambitious, able to concentrate and to take the long view. Rational, rigorous, objective intelligence. Geometrical, abstract aptitude. Quiet in love, detached but faithful; tends toward celibacy.[9]

Reading the above quote we see the outlines of a well-defined personality. Everyone knows people like that; the description is psychologically consistent and convincing. The absurdity consists in claiming that such a personality type occurs more frequently in people who are born between December 21 and January 19. There are of course no serious proofs for this assertion. But the psychological patterns of the astrologers are quite sophisticated; they can be easily adapted to fit the appearance of any customer, so that the latter becomes convinced that he is dealing with real sorcery. There is no doubt that among the 60 per cent of the population who know their birth sign, many identify with the corresponding psychological type to the point of really believing in a close resemblance.

Influence on Everyday Language

Even those who are indifferent, or even hostile, to astrology cannot avoid mentioning it in their everyday conversation. Our life is punctuated by constant astrological reminders. Look at the calendar: there are twelve months in a year, just as many as there are zodiacal signs; the month is the period that divides two new moons (month and moon have the same etymological origin); the four weeks of the month derive from the four quarters of the moon. "Adopted by the church, in spite of its suspicious origin, it [the nomenclature for the days of the week] was imposed on all Christian peoples," writes the historian Franz Cumont. "When today we name the days Saturday, Sunday, Monday, we are heathen and astrologers without knowing it, since we recognize implicitly that the first belongs to Saturn, the second to the Sun, and the third to the Moon."[10] This astrological tradition is kept alive in most other languages. Tuesday is *Mardi* in French and *Martedi* in Italian, meaning the day of Mars; Wednesday is called *Mercredi* and *Mercoledi*, or the day of Mercury; Thursday is *Jeudi* and *Giovedi* after Jupiter, leaving Friday, *Vendredi* and *Venerdi*, in the care of Venus.

The great religious festivities on our calendars have similar astrological origins. They are modifications of ancient solar feasts: Christmas is celebrated at the winter solstice, when the days that have been getting shorter begin to lengthen again. In fact, the birth of Christ heralds a new era, just as the New Year does. And Christ's Resurrection is remembered at Easter, when Nature itself is born again to spring after the winter sleep. Even today the Church changes the exact date of Easter from year to

year, following the changes of the moon, to coincide with
the Sunday following the first full moon after the equi-
nox of spring.

And there is more: as Cumont has said,

> There can perhaps be no more striking proof of the
> power and popularity of astrological beliefs than the
> influence which they have exercised over popular lan-
> guage. All modern idioms have preserved traces of it,
> which we can no longer discern save with difficulty,
> survivals of vanished superstitions. Do we still remem-
> ber, when we speak of a martial, jovial, or lunatic
> character, that it must have been formed by Mars,
> Jupiter, or the Moon, that an *influence* is the effect
> of a fluid emitted by the celestial bodies, that it is one
> of these 'astra' which, if hostile, will cause me a 'dis-
> aster,' and that, finally, if I have good fortune to find
> myself among you, I certainly owe it to my lucky star?[11]

The Stare of the Stars

How did the unlikely mixture of beliefs that consti-
tutes astrological doctrine survive and prosper up to our
days? It is an important question, one the discoveries of
psychology are just beginning to explain.

It is difficult for us modern men, who "know" how the
universe is run, to see the outside world with fresh eyes.
The Chaldean priests five thousand years ago certainly
did not see it as we do. As they climbed to the summit of
their watchtowers, it seemed to them that the stars were
within reach of their outstretched arms. For them the
stars had wills, feelings, distinct personalities.

Psychologists have shown that children, with the
naiveté of ignorance, perceive the world more the way the
ancient Chaldeans did than as modern adults do. For

children, the sun and the moon are alive and conscious. The Swiss psychologist Piaget has questioned hundreds of children in his investigations. Below a certain age, the answers he received were always the same. Jacques, aged six, was asked about the sun:

> "Does it move?"
> "Sure. When we walk, it follows. When we turn, it turns, too."
> "Why does it move?"
> "Because when we walk, it walks."
> "Why does it walk?"
> "To hear what we are saying."
> "Is it alive?"
> "Sure it's alive! Otherwise it couldn't follow us; it couldn't shine."[12]

Here are the answers given by Michel, eight years old, when asked about the moon:

> "Can the moon do what it wants?"
> "Yes, when we walk, it follows us."
> "Does it follow you or does it stay put?"
> "It follows. It stops if I stop."
> "If I walk too, whom will it follow?"
> "Me."
> "Who?"
> "You."
> "Do you think it follows everybody?"
> "Yes."
> "It can be everywhere at the same time?"
> "Yes."[13]

To Jacques and Michel the optical illusion that is so familiar to adults that they forget to notice it means that the sun and the moon have a personality, a will of their own.

The sky appears so close to a child that he believes that a lariat would enable him to catch a star. This quote from William James is a good example:

> He believed the sun to be a ball of fire. First he thought there were several suns, one for each day. He couldn't understand how they could rise and set. One evening, he saw by chance some boys who were throwing burning balls of twine drenched in oil up in the air. After this he believed that the sun must be thrown up and caught in the same manner. But who had such strength? So he assumed that there must be a big and strong man hiding somewhere behind the hills (the child was living in San Francisco). The sun was the ball of fire he used for a toy, and he amused himself by throwing it high up in the sky each morning and catching it every evening. . . . He assumed that the God (the big, strong man) also lighted the stars for his personal use, as we do with the gas lights.[14]

Such childlike images are very close to those held by the first observers of the heavens. The ancient Egyptians, for instance, thought that

> the fixed stars were lamps, suspended from the vault, or carried by other gods. The planets sailed in their own boats along canals originating in the Milky Way, the celestial twin of the Nile. Towards the fifteenth of each month, the moon god was attacked by a ferocious sow, and devoured in a fortnight of agony; then he was reborn again. Sometimes the sow swallowed him whole, causing a lunar eclipse; sometimes a serpent swallowed the sun, causing a solar eclipse.[15]

Children gradually learn to mistrust appearances and, through contact with adults, form for themselves an accurate image of the world. In this they benefit from the accumulated knowledge of mankind. But didn't the

Chaldean have good reasons for explaining the world as he did? Every day the sun *seems* to follow its own path in crossing the blue dome of heaven, dying in the evening only to be reborn in the morning: how could it shine eternally if it did not have a divine essence? The moon *appears* to be cutting itself thinner and thinner, and then to be growing again from nothing. The star glittering in the haze at the edge of the horizon *seems* to be winking at us.

The Denial of Chance

Another thing children share with men of the past is the belief that nothing occurs by chance.

> Christian, eight years old, often plays with a small toy roulette. One day, he was shown a similar toy which was loaded: after each turn the ball stopped without fail on the same number. This did not surprise the boy at all. When he was asked how this happened, he answered with assurance: "Easy! The ball wants to stop on that number. There's nothing to it."[16]

For the child, just as for the gambler, chance does not exist. The ball *chooses* to stop in one place or the other; some sort of intrinsic will dwells in the object enabling it to change its behavior.

Chance does not exist for the astrologer either. The stars determine every round of our lives up to the second of our death. One astrologer explained the death of Napoleon as follows: "The moon was passing his planet, which was in the eighth sector. This was Venus, seven degrees from Cancer; and the moon conveyed on Venus the opposition that Uranus and Neptune were concentrating on it from their location three degrees from Capricorn."[17] To the astrologer, Napoleon had no hope of surviving May 5, 1821, the day on which the planets had woven their inescapable network of influences for him.

But what if a prediction made in advance does not turn out the way the astrologer has foreseen? In such a case there is no chance involved either: "When human prevision fails, it is God's will that is being carried out," says an Egyptian papyrus of the fifth dynasty, about 4000 B.C.

Unconscious Projection

Current astrology shares with the thought of the ancients a childlike simplicity applied to the problems of grown-up life. Yet it would be very misleading to see the Chaldeans as nothing but big children. They were also matchless observers of the sky. Their patience, the precision of their calculations, and the systematic nature of their reports show them to be civilized adults. But they also felt the problems and terrors of being exposed to the dangers and mystery of the world, and so they created idols, which they hoped to propitiate.

Why were the divinities of their faith placed in the sky? In Mesopotamia clouds very rarely cover the stars; faced with their wonderful sparkling, men found it easy to believe that the flashing planets were the glances of the gods. So these gazing stars were thought to have some of man's feelings and fears. Freud gave the name "projection" to the unconscious psychological mechanism that makes us see in others the feelings we ourselves dimly experience. The French philosopher Gaston Bachelard has expressed this unconscious projection of human concerns into the sky perfectly:

> On the vast dark canvas of the night, mathematical half-dreaming has drawn sketches. They are so wrong,

so deliciously wrong, all these constellations! They include in the same figure completely alien stars. Between
a few real points, between the stars isolated like lone
diamonds, the dream draws imaginary lines. Dream,
that great priest of abstract painting, sees all the animals of the zodiac in these few scattered points. *Homo
faber*—the lazy cartwright—sees a carriage without
wheels in the sky; the farmer dreaming about his crops
sees a golden sheaf of wheat. . . . The zodiac is the
Rorschach test of mankind in its infancy.[18]

If man projects himself into the sky, he ends by identi-
fying with it, with the constellation he is most related to.
Thus someone born under the constellation of Libra
sees himself as being just and well-balanced, like the
plates of a scale. One born under Scorpio imagines himself to be, like the animal of his sign, dangerous, biting,
aggressive, and sometimes capable of turning his aggres-
sion against himself.

Answers Through Ignorance

It would be foolish to be excessively harsh with these
naive associations. The trail the ancients blazed was without doubt necessary. It opened a road for us. The explanation of the world that the Chaldeans constructed
was incomparably better for them than our explanation
would have been. It would have made no sense to them
to imagine a universe filled with galaxies escaping from
the earth at speeds increasing as a function of their distance.

As John V. Campbell has written in *Analog*:

Astrology started several millennia ago, when early
men first observed the immense effect the cycles of the
stars had on events here on earth. The early Egyptians

and Babylonians had not the slightest conception *why*
the world grew colder when the cycle of the stars
brought Orion rising in the east at twilight—or *why*
the world grew warmer again when Lyra rose at dusk,
and Orion was no longer visible. . . . But then, they
didn't know *why* planting a seed caused a plant to come
up. When the world is one vast collection of mysteries,
the business of a wise man is to establish some sound,
reliable correlations, letting the questions of *why* go until he has more information.[19]

The Greeks were the first to question the origin of
things seriously. We still admire the answers they were
able to give in a variety of fields. But to explain how astrology may have worked was not an easy task. The most
obvious theory was to assume that the stars acted through
"effluvia" descending to earth. "As examples of such effluvia, they cited the attraction of amber on straw, the
killing stare of the basilisk, the wolf's stare which makes
man dumb. It was more difficult to believe in the effluvia
of imaginary entities, like the constellations."[20] Yet to
those who believed in astrology, the effluvia were a better
explanation for the stars' ability to act across remote distances than the theory of universal gravitation is to modern man, since we know the effects of this force but still
do not know its nature.

The passionate attempt to explain the destiny of men
and the world by way of the stars has failed, because men
have lacked the knowledge to pose the crucial questions
correctly. As Koestler wrote,

> But on reflection, what other explanation was there
> available at the time? To a questing mind without an
> inkling of the processes by which heredity and environ-
> ment shape a man's character, astrology, in one form
> or another, was the obvious means of relating the in-
> dividual to the universal whole, by making him reflect

the all-embracing constellation of the world, by establishing an intimate sympathy and correspondence between microcosmos and macrocosmos.[21]

The Uncertain Future

Man is no longer Chaldean, he is no longer a child. He knows and uses the new technologies science has brought within his reach. "Cosmology has become an exact science. . . . The wild dance of shadows that the stars projected on the walls of Plato's cave has changed to a stately waltz,"[22] writes Koestler. Since 1957 hundreds of man-made satellites have been circling the earth. We have become used to the thought that the moon and the planets will one day become our suburbs. The mysterious dread those who scanned the sky in the past felt is no longer familiar to us.

Moreover, in the large cities it has become almost impossible to see the sky. In New York, when the skyscrapers light up at night, how is one to tell the pale reflection of Venus or Mars from the artificial lights filling the heavens? Even the astronomers have given up: they have removed their observatories to less densely populated regions, to the tops of mountains.

Those who live in cities are therefore less and less interested in the appearance of the sky. For them, it has become a familiar, reassuring object. The complex pattern underlying the movement of the stars has long since been deciphered. Modern man, even if he is not especially versed in astronomy, has substituted the well-regulated mechanism of Keplerian ellipses for the terrors of the spheres.

And yet the future remains uncertain; fate remains outside our control. "Miserable and bold mortals: we measure the course of the stars, and after all the painstaking research, we are still unknown to ourselves," cried the famous preacher Bossuet to King Louis XIV and his assembled court.[23]

Our security has not increased since then. A recent survey has shown that in the past twenty years there have been forty wars all over the world. Today's well being may be followed by a catastrophe tomorrow. At this point, neither political leaders nor scientists can solve these difficulties. By contrast, the astrologers claim that they could do so. They promise to predict which will be the lean years and which will be the fat ones. To the astrologer and his client, the movement of the stars is not a pretense. If an unforeseen war did explode, it would not mean that the sky had come unhinged but that humanity had. Of course, everyday life contains unavoidable misfortunes and problems one cannot solve alone. Under these circumstances it is understandable that man should attempt to find comfort wherever it is promised. The astrologer often acts as a spiritual father, a role that neatly allows the client to decline any responsibility of his own. When one has tried everything in vain, or when something is obviously impossible, then one consults the astrologer. He helps those who, as the French expression goes, "wish to have the moon."

Shakespeare has left a masterful portrait of such a state of mind in *King Lear:*

> This is the excellent foppery of the world, that, when we are sick in fortune, often the surfeit of our own behaviour, we make guilty of our disasters the sun, the moon, and the stars; as if we were villains by necessity, fools by heavenly compulsion; knaves, thieves, and treachers by spherical predominance; drunkards, liars, and adulterers by an enforc'd obedience of planetary influence; and all that we are evil in, by a divine thrust-

ing on. An admirable evasion of whoremaster man, to lay his goatish disposition to the charge of a star! My father compounded with my mother under the Dragon's Tail, and my nativity was under Ursa Major, so that it follows I am rough and lecherous. Fut! I should have been that I am, had the maidenliest star in the firmament twinkled on my bastardizing.[24]

The fatalistic tendency to blame the stars for one's failures, instead of attempting to remedy them through personal effort, has been denounced by psychologists. In 1940, the following declaration was published by the American Association of Social and Psychological Studies:

> The principal reason which turns some men to astrology and other superstitions is that they lack the necessary resources to solve the serious problems with which they are faced. Frustrated, they give in to the pleasant suggestion that there is a golden key within their reach, a simple solution, an ever present help in times of trouble.[25]

Faith in astrology today is therefore the symptom of a social and psychological disorder—a grave symptom. Man is looking for something progress has failed to provide so far; it is perhaps a search for the meaning of life. As the historian Peuckert writes:

> Whether I believe my newspaper or my church, or look for an answer among the stars, I still have the uncomfortable feeling "that there is something up there" which "may fall on my neck." It is the uncertainty of man thrown into the world, feeling surrounded, fearing a hostile will, who, faced with a God who refuses to speak and scientists who just shrug their shoulders, hides behind the first answer someone gives him.[26]

NOTES TO CHAPTER FIVE

1. G. Schmidtchen, "Soziologisches über die Astrologie. Ergebnisse einer repräsentativ-Befragung," *Z. f. Parapsychologie u. Grenzgebiete der Psychologie*, I (1957), 47.

2. L. MacNeice, *Astrology* (London: Aldus Books, 1964).

3. "Astrology, Sense or Nonsense?" *Life International*, March 28, 1960.

4. E. Leoni, *Nostradamus: Life and Literature* (New York: Nosbooks, 1961).

5. E. Howe, *Urania's Children: The Strange World of the Astrologers* (London: William Kimber, 1967).

6. C. G. Jung, *The Spiritual Problem of Modern Man*, Collected Works, Vol. X (New York: Pantheon, 1964).

7. Enquête de l'Institut Français d'Opinion Publique, "Tout ce qu'il y a derrière votre horoscope," *France-Soir*, January, 1963.

8. Schmidtchen, *op. cit.*

9. A. Barbault, *Défense et illustration de l'astrologie* (Paris: Grasset, 1955).

10. F. Cumont, *Astrology and Religion Among the Greeks and Romans* (New York: Dover, 1960).

11. *Ibid.*

12. J. Piaget, *La représentation du monde chez l'enfant* (Paris: P.U.F., 1947).

13. *Ibid.*

14. W. James, "Thought Before Language," *Philosophical Review*, I (1892), 613.

15. A. Koestler, *The Sleepwalkers* (New York: Macmillan, 1959).

16. M. and F. Gauquelin, *La psychologie au XX⁰ siècle* (Paris: Editions Sociales Françaises, 1963).

17. A. Barbault, *Traité pratique d'astrologie* (Paris: Le Seuil, 1961).

18. G. Bachelard, *L'air et les songes* (Paris: J. Corti).

19. J. V. Campbell, "Astrologer-Astronomer-Astroengineer," *Analog*, September 18, 1962.

20. A. Bouché-Leclercq, *L'astrologie grecque* (Paris: Leroux, 1899).

21. Koestler, *op. cit.*
22. *Ibid.*
23. B. Bossuet, *Sermon sur la loi de Dieu.*
24. W. Shakespeare, *King Lear,* Act I, Scene 2.
25. P. Couderc, *L'astrologie* (Paris: P.U.F., 1951).
26. W. Peuckert, *L'astrologie* (Paris: Payot, 1965).

The Scientific Process

IN EVERY method of telling the future save astrology, *divination* is a *divine* revelation, a kind of extension of the human intellect. Astrology, on the other hand, began to break off from the religious attitude which created it, and instead of *divining* it pretended to *predict*, and in so doing usurped the prestigious first rank among the natural sciences.[1]

This definition by the historian Bouché-Leclercq clearly indicates how embarrassing and irritating the issue of astrology must be to a scientist of the twentieth century. If astrology had remained the religion of universal harmonies it was in the beginning, the scientist, who knows the limitations of his method, would not have become involved with a problem outside his competence. Everyone is free to believe in the religion of his choice. But astrological faith is a peculiar one. It is "a faith which uses the language of science, and a science that finds the basis of its principles in faith."[2]

Because astrology employs a language that pretends to be scientific, because it bases its predictions on the accurate computations of the astronomers, and because it deals with the empirical objects of the celestial bodies, science has the duty of assessing the value of current astrological methods and their results.

Strange Determinism

Astrology, like science, is based on a deterministic assumption: that causes are followed by effects. In astrology the "cause" is the horoscope, a momentary configuration of celestial bodies. The "effect" is the fate of the person to whom the horoscope applies. The implications of such a deterministic view were explored by an astronomer:

> Astrological predictions assume the existence of a long-range determinism which constitutes an outrageous caricature of scientific determinism. Let's suppose that an eighty-year-old man slides on an orange peel and kills himself. Obviously, this event and its causes can be accounted for in terms of the laws of mechanics. But even the most rabid determinist would not claim that eighty years earlier it had been possible to predict, even if all the information in the world had been available, that the embryonic old man and the future orange peel were destined to clash in the future. Instead we say that the accident was due to *chance,* because an infinity of *independent* events have contributed to its occurrence. So many fortuitous circumstances modify our behavior each second that it is impossible to predict such an accident even one minute in advance. It is even more remarkable, then, to explain the cause of the fall by associating it with the position of some celestial bodies eighty years before, when the poor man had just been born.[3]

How does astrology determine the nature of the influence in question? What law explains the beneficial influence of Jupiter, and the evil one of Saturn? Why is their quadratic relationship bad, but their trigon good for the future? Both are just big masses of rocks surrounded by gases, two unconscious bodies. How can one justify the association of ideas that connects the purely imaginary shape of the zodiacal figures with the supposed influence of the planets on the signs, and vice-versa? Astronomy has known for a long time that planets are a great distance from any of the constellations, and that they look as if they are "inside" constellations only because of the misleading effects of perspective.

Terrestrial Causes of Destiny

If one tries to look at astrology scientifically, one is constantly confronted by a wall of logical contradictions. Astrologers have not been able to explain by what miracle the stars at birth are able to overthrow all the weight of heredity and the constraints of the social environment. Because astrology was born at a time when both these factors were unknown, it ignored them; and it still does:

> The specifics of a man's health or personality are not attributed to his genetic heredity, to his chromosomes, to his grandparent's vices, or to the education he received or the social environment in which he has lived. Instead, they are credited to the signs of the zodiac and to the planets which, like fairy godmothers, decide on a man's destiny by hovering around his crib.[4]

The discoveries of psychoanalysis explain some of our unconscious acts, which often rule our destinies. In the past, these acts were attributed to the stars because it was not known that their origins were deep within man. Yet the German poet Schiller intuitively felt the correct causal relation when he made one of his characters say: "The stars of your destiny are within your heart!"

A further instance of bad logic consists in the fact that if the stars did have anything to do with one's fate, their effect ought to be felt at the time of conception rather than at birth—perhaps by influencing the chromosomal distribution in the gametes of the parents. Greek astrology felt this problem. Ptolemy in his *Tetrabiblos* recognized that it would be vastly preferable to draw horoscopes for the time of conception, but he was unable to do anything about it because of the difficulty in determining the exact date of conception. Finally he rationalized the use of the birth horoscope as follows: "When the fruit is perfect, nature moves it so that it will be born under the same constellation which reigned at the time of conception" (Book III, 1). This assertion is wholly gratuitous, and although its truth has never been demonstrated by astrologers, it does not bother them excessively even today.

The problem posed by twins is another stumbling-block for astrology. Twins often share the same fate, but, as Dr. Kallmann of the Psychiatric Institute of New York has shown, this happens only when they develop from the same egg, in which case they are, genetically, the same individual reproduced twice. Despite their identical birthdate, twins born of two separate eggs have as varied careers as brothers or sisters born at intervals of several years. In the same vein, nobody has succeeded in showing similarities in the lives of people born the same day of different parents. Some authors have attempted to demonstrate such a relationship; the Swiss astrologer K.E. Krafft coined the expression "twins under the stars" to describe such people. But social conditions explain the pattern of a life better than the stars do. Of all the boys

born on the afternoon of May 17, 1917, only one became
President of the United States.

Astronomical Impossibilities

Astrology, begun in latitudes relatively close to the
equator, made no provisions for the possibility that no
planet may be in sight for several weeks in a row. Yet
this condition prevails above the Arctic Circle (66 degrees latitude); there it is usually impossible to compute
the zodiacal point rising on the horizon, which is necessary in making a horoscope. As civilization advances,
towns are built in inhospitable surroundings; children
in increasing numbers are born in the Arctic regions. It
would be absurd to believe that all the young Alaskans,
Canadians, Greenlanders, Norwegians, Finns, and Si-
berians would benefit from no celestial influences, if
these are to determine their lives.

But faith in astrology has weathered similar objections
in the past: for instance, the discovery of the procession
of the equinoxes in the second century B.C. by Hipparcus.
Here is how a contemporary astronomer describes this
phenomenon:

> A slow oscillation of the alignment of the poles
> changes the celestial equator among the constellations.
> Since the times of Hipparcus, the gamma-point (the
> first degree of Ram) has retraced its way through the
> entire constellation of the Fishes, carrying behind it-
> self the whole network of zodiacal rectangles with their
> old names.[5]

In other words, the zodiac is now like an apartment house
where each occupant moved down one floor but left his
name-plate on the old door. The signs of the zodiac have
slipped about one case since Ptolemy. When the sun is

said to be crossing the constellation of Libra, it is in fact traversing Scorpio. But the tradition-bound astrologers keep attributing to the child born at such a time the influences of Libra, since they did not keep count of astronomical procession. When confronted with this objection,

> the astrologers answer that the virtues are a function of a *sign,* not of a constellation; but it is somewhat hilarious that the virtues of each sign should express exactly the supposed qualities of the mythical beast that today dwells in the preceding rectangle of the zodiac.[6]

Finally, modern astrologers show an amazing lack of interest in the medical aspects of the birth process. It has often been pointed out that a premature birth, or one caused by surgical intervention, could not possibly reveal the newborn's destiny, because it was the doctor's decision that determined the hour of his birth. The tendency nowadays is more and more in the direction of inducing labor with drugs, "and this would change the astral influences on the baby's destiny, making his whole future life an artificial one."[7]

And besides, how is one to tell which is the "right" astrology? The symbolism of the stars varies from culture to culture. The Indian and Chinese zodiacs consist of animals different from those in the Western ones, which derive from the Greco-Chaldean zodiacs. For instance, the Chaldeans represented Capricorn as a goat with the lower body of a fish; this symbol is still used, although the emphasis is almost entirely on the goat. In India and China, on the other hand, Capricorn is represented by a bear and a unicorn, respectively.

There must be very few people who, deep down, do not see the anachronisms of astrology. But the believers claim that rational objections are ultimately beside the point. They do not practice a science, but an occult art; and occultism need not concern itself with modern discoveries. What really counts, after all, is whether a system works or whether it does not. If astrological predictions turn out to be true, if the pattern of stars at birth actually correlates with patterns in the life of man, what more could we ask of astrology? Science has recently accepted this challenge. A truth serum has been given to astrology: the method for the computation of probability.

Astrology and Probability

The computation of probability is based on the study of the laws of chance, which, contrary to what was believed in the past, *does* exist. Not only does it exist, it obeys certain measurable laws, which mathematics has only recently tamed. The practical application of the "laws of chance" is what we call the statistical method. It is only in the last fifty years that this method has been used to any good effect. Now it is beginning to help us establish, in many different fields, where random events end and regular laws begin.

How can the statistical method be used in astrology? Let us take an example. Astrology claims that children born under the sign of Libra will possess artistic qualities because this sign is ruled by Venus, the planet of the arts and of beauty. Therefore children who are born while the sun is passing through the sign of Libra (from September 21 to October 21) should become painters or musicians in greater numbers than children born under the other signs of the zodiac. What we can do, then, is to take a volume of biographies and list all the birthdates of known artists. Then we note the zodiacal signs under which the artists were born. If astrologers are right, there will be many more artists born under the sign of Libra; if they are wrong, the number under Libra will not exceed that under the other zodiacal signs. The results thus obtained can then be analyzed by mathematical formulas developed from the probability theory. These formulas will show whether the number of artists born under Libra is large enough to reflect an actual trend rather than a random event. The statistical method has nothing to do with the personal opinion of the researcher, which is replaced by a figure that tells us whether there is or is not an astrological law.

One scientist, Farnsworth,

> has had the patience to study the birth dates of more than two thousand famous painters and musicians: Libra has not ruled over the birth of these people more than the other signs. The supposed correlation does not exist; in fact, chance made the correlation come out negative; that is, Libra had fewer than its quota of artists.[8]

A commission of the American Association of Scientific Societies devoted several years to a study of the astrological laws submitted to it. Under the chairmanship of the eminent Harvard astronomer Bart J. Bok, the results of the inquest were published, with the conclusion that "none of the influences alleged by the astrologers were verified."[9] Astronomer J. Allen Hynek studied the birthdates of scientists included in *American Men of Science*. The distribution of the dates according to zodiacal signs fell into a random pattern. Seasonal variations in the number of births, which as Huntington has discovered occur in every population, were also found by

Hynek; but these have nothing to do with astrology. In Europe, the Belgian Committee for the Investigation of So-called Paranormal Phenomena, which consists of thirty scientists from various disciplines, concluded a recent investigation as follows: "Not one of the cases submitted by astrologers deals with an experience worthy to be called scientific."

Our Systematic Researches

In France we have been involved for several years in a systematic verification of astrological propositions. Some of our conclusions were published in 1955 under the title of *Astral Influences: A Critical and Experimental Study*.[10, 11] Those who are interested in the detailed reporting of data should consult that work; here we will only summarize briefly the gist of the findings.

Our first task was to evaluate the statistical methods employed by the astrologers themselves. Their techniques were found to be severely limited: the laws of chance are ignored and conclusions are reached without support. The researches conducted by the "Church of Lights" in Los Angeles, by D. Bradley in the U.S., and by Von Klocker in Germany cannot be called scientific. The *Astrobiological Treatise* by K.E. Krafft, which made some impact when it was first published in 1939, deserves no more confidence.[12] We devoted about thirty pages to an extensive criticism of the *Treatise*,[13] and concluded that it contains no law in the scientific sense. The work of the French astrologer Paul Choisnard (1867–1930) deserves more attention, since he attempted to prove the myth of astrology more systematically, through statistics. He was the first astrologer to propose the employment of this technique, in his *Proofs and Bases of Scientific As-*

trology.[14] We examined all the proofs offered by Choisnard and will give an example of their worth. He claimed, for instance, that there is "obvious proof that people die under particular celestial configurations." After studying two hundred cases, he concluded that when death occurred "Mars was three times, and Saturn twice as often in conjunction with the sun in the position of the person's birth, than at any other period." We checked this statement by assembling a much larger sample than the one Choisnard used and comparing the birth and the death horoscopes of seven thousand individuals; no trace was found of the supposedly adverse influences of Mars and Saturn. The number of critical conjunctions found for these two planets was well within the limits of chance.[15] Similarly, all the statements proposed by Choisnard were shown to lack foundation; the statistical laws of chance in every case superseded the purported laws of astrology.

The Fate of Criminals

Another step in our research was to calculate the horoscopes of more than fifty thousand people whose lives indicated some exceptional characteristic—a special aptitude, or gift, or stroke of luck—and also those whose lives were marred by exceptionally adverse conditions. For all these people we noted not only the day but also the hour of birth.

In no case did we find a statistically significant difference favoring the traditional laws of astrology. As an example, in our report of 1955 we included a sample of criminals. The reddish planet Mars is considered to be connected with violence, crime, and blood. It should therefore appear in a foremost position in the horoscope of criminals. A contemporary astrologer has expressed this belief as follows:

> Mars makes one impulsive, aggressive, tyrannical. It rules tempers, and also iron and fire; objects which are hard, sharp, or dangerous. It rules the passions and battles of life; the enmities, betrayals, losses, trials, surgical operations, and accidents.[16]

Therefore we obtained the vital statistics of all French criminals on record at the Paris Courthouse. We selected the files of 623 murderers who, according to the judgment of experts, were the most notorious in the annals of justice for the horror of their crimes. Most of them died under the guillotine. When their horoscopes were cast, it was shown that Mars was not particularly strong among these arch-criminals. The following table shows the distribution of Mars in the twelve astrological houses at the time of their birth:

TABLE I
Position of the Planet Mars in the Horoscope of Criminals

(The first row of figures refers to the number of criminals in each house; the second row reports the number expected to be in each house if chance were operating only in terms of astronomical and demographic laws.)

Astrological House	I	II	III	IV	V	VI	VII	VIII	IX	X	XI	XII
Number Observed	60	51	58	59	58	38	49	48	47	53	48	54
Number Expected	55	54	51	50	49	48	50	51	52	53	54	56

The positions of Mars are evenly distributed among the twelve astrological houses, following the random pattern very closely; none of the figures differs significantly from the theoretical numbers expected by chance. It is rather disappointing for astrological theory that criminals are not born more often with Mars in "the eighth house"—that of death for oneself or for others; or in "the twelfth house," which rules over "trials and gaols." As can be seen, these two houses contain perfectly average numbers.[17]

None of the astrologers we studied passed the classic test known as "the test of opposed destinies." The test consists of forty birthdates, twenty of well-known criminals and twenty of persons who led a long and peaceful life. The astrologers' task is to separate the two groups of people on the basis of their birth horoscope. The result is always great confusion: the astrologers invariably select a mixed bag of criminals and peaceful citizens in about the same proportions that a machine would by picking randomly. We should add that only sincerely believing astrologers agreed to take our test in the first place; the immense majority of charlatans always find a likely excuse to avoid a confrontation that might endanger their credibility in the public eye.[18]

The Verdict

Modern astrology, as a predictive method, relies on the survival of a hopelessly outdated view of the world and of life. It ignores the progress of astronomy and of human biology, as well as all the variables that affect behavior through a lifetime. Every effort made by astrologers to defend their basic postulate, that the movement of the stars can predict destiny, has failed. Whenever such predictions are examined by impartial scientific committees, the supposed accuracy that astrology claims soon evaporates. Statistics have disposed of old arguments once and for all: the numbers speak without bias, and they leave no room for doubt. Whoever claims to predict the future by consulting the stars is fooling either himself or someone else.

A prestigious astronomical society, the Astronomische Gesellschaft, came out a few years ago with the following verdict:

> The belief that the position of the stars at birth influences the future of the newborn, and that one can find advice in private and public matters in the stars, rests on a view of the universe which places the earth and its inhabitants at the hub of the universe. This conception has been refuted a long time ago. What are today called astrology, cosmology, and so on, are nothing but a mixture of superstition, fakery, and exploitation. There is a group of astrologers who denounce the majority practice of mass-producing printed horoscopes dealing with every aspect of life, and try to oppose such nonsense with a presumably seriously scientific astrology, but their efforts have not succeeded in proving that their pursuits are any more scientific.[19]

NOTES TO CHAPTER SIX

1. A. Bouché-Leclercq, *L'astrologie grecque* (Paris: Leroux, 1899).
2. *Ibid.*
3. P. Couderc, *L'astrologie* (Paris: P.U.F., 1951).
4. *Ibid.*
5. *Ibid.*
6. *Ibid.*
7. *Ibid.*
8. *Ibid.*
9. *Ibid.*
10. M. Gauquelin, *L'influence des astres, étude critique et experimentale* (Paris: Le Dauphin, 1955).
11. ———, "Der Einfluss der Gestirne und die Statistik," *Z.f. Parapsychologie u. Grenzgebiete der Psychologie,* I (1957), 23.
12. K.E. Krafft, *Traité d'Astrobiologie* (Paris: Legrand, 1939).
13. Gauquelin, *L'influence des astres, op. cit.*
14. P. Choisnard, *Preuves et bases de l'astrologie scientifique* (Paris: Chacornac, 1921).
15. Gauquelin, *L'influence des astres, op. cit.*
16. A. Barbault, *Défense et illustration de l'astrologie* (Paris: Grasset, 1955).
17. Gauquelin, *L'influence des astres, étude critique et experimentale, op.cit.*
18. M. Gauquelin, *L'astrologie devant la science* (Paris: Planète, 1965).
19. Couderc, *op. cit.*

Blocked Matrices

AFTER *establishing the illusory nature of the belief in astrological prediction, the scientist may still remain dissatisfied. After all, he knows that in the history of ideas, magic always precedes science, that the intuition of phenomena anticipates their objective knowledge. He feels intuitively, as men have always felt, that astrology may contain some truths.*

No one denies, for instance, that the sun constantly influences us and that without it life on earth would be impossible. Everyone knows, as the ancients did, that "the greedy sucking of the moon pulls the sea after itself" (Pliny), that the junction of the sun and of the moon causes vast pulsations in the ocean. There is then an interaction between these bodies and the earth. Doesn't one have the duty to go further? Can it really be useless to expect that the cosmos influences life in yet other ways, ways that for centuries have been buried under the growths of ignorance and mystification?

There is a brilliant description in Koestler's The Act of Creation *of what he calls the "blocked matrices" of science. In various historical periods a given branch of science ceases to develop further. It may become atrophied, blocked sometimes for several centuries. The reason for such arrests is often a psychological one. A good*

88

*example of a blocked matrix is the stagnant state in which
cosmological systems remained between the end of antiquity and the Renaissance, when, as Koestler writes,
"the eyes of astronomers for centuries were bombarded
with the facts that prove that the planets' movements
depend on the movements of the sun. But the astronomers preferred to look elsewhere." Today, a great number of scientific researchers have become interested in
solving the mystery of astral influences. In this task they
are faced with matrices as blocked as those confronted
by Copernicus, Galileo, Newton, Darwin, or Einstein.
Astrology is a branch of learning that was closed almost
as soon as it was opened. It may seem foolish to try to
revive it after so many centuries. But for the history of
thought the passing centuries are a short time indeed.*

In the fourth century B.C., *the Greek astronomer
Aristarcus of Samos, having realized that the sun was
much larger than the earth, developed a heliocentric
theory in which the sun was at the center of the planetary
system. But this thin thread of truth was soon to
break: in the first century of our era Ptolemy, in
his treatise on world systems, the* Almageste, *put the
earth back in the center of the universe. Almost twenty
centuries had to pass before Copernicus again took
up Aristarcus' old idea and Kepler discovered that the
planets gravitated around the sun in elliptical orbits.
Also in the fourth century* B.C., *Hippocrates, the father
of modern medicine, developed an interpretation of
man's dependence on weather and the planets that approximates the modern science of biometeorology. Then
again the thread was broken and knowledge degenerated
into superstition, under the influence of Ptolemy's* Tetrabiblos, *which laid the foundation for contemporary
fortune-telling.*

Nineteen centuries have elapsed since the Tetrabiblos *—a period not substantially longer than the one that separated Ptolemy's epicycles from Kepler's ellipses. The progress of astronomy has so far discredited the notion that the cosmos could influence the earth and its inhabitants. "Ether," the magical, living substance that was assumed to extend from the earth's surface to the stars, was replaced in the nineteenth century with empty and sterile "outer space." But the continued efforts of science in the twentieth century have again brought us closer to the intuition of the far-away past. Artificial satellites have shown that "outer space" is not really empty but filled with various fields of force that constantly affect the earth.*

In the last few years, researchers have finally reopened the blocked matrices of astrology and replaced it with a new science. They have succeeded in spanning the sixty centuries that separate the anxious queries of primitive man from the discovery of precise and extremely subtle influences on our lives. Science has supervised similar mergers in the past by incorporating what used to be only superstition. The share left to the fortune-tellers shrinks every year. In this century whole domains of the occult have been conquered by science, beginning with the "key to the dreams." Freud and Jung pioneered in this area, by reproaching science for having stopped at the thresholds of the illogical.

As a matter of fact, science knows more about man's future now than the astrologers ever hoped to be able to foretell in their most exalted dreams. Psychology, sociology, genetics, and statistics are now able to tame and even control chance. In December, 1965, the French Institute for Public Opinion correctly predicted the exact percentage of votes cast for General de Gaulle eight days before the elections took place. There was no need for divination, although it may seem somewhat miraculous that it should be possible to predict the behavior of twenty million voters by interviewing only a few thousand. But the laws of chance are winning out over the randomness of the past; even the future of the world is scientifically predictable with the help of electronic equipment. There is no further need for Nostradamus: the Rand Corporation recently published a detailed account of the major future discoveries of humanity, even specifying the approximate date for each.

This is why it should not be surprising that scientific researchers have succeeded in converting astrology into a science. Although they still have to battle to have their discoveries accepted, scientists in the field are slowly replacing the art of prophecy with objective observation. Atmospheric catastrophies have yielded almost completely: the progress of meteorology allows several days' notice in the sighting of a hurricane on the Florida coast; here the barometer has replaced predictions derived from the appearance of the moon god. It is, in fact, through success in the prediction of the weather that former attitudes toward cosmic influences have softened and become more receptive. Thus a review of weather prediction is a logical starting point in our survey of the new discoveries in the field of cosmic influence.

The stage is now set for the last act of the cosmic drama, the most interesting and beautiful one. The rule of superstition ends here. A new science will replace the old cabala of cosmic dreams; it will help us to assess man's true place in the riddle of the universe. We are indeed living through a turning-point in human thought.

PART
TWO

Weather Forecasting

T HE PREDICTION of weather is the first field in which science has replaced astrological prediction. Less than a hundred years ago meteorological observatories were first built in the major cities around the world. At the beginning, only temperature, humidity, wind velocity, and variations in barometric pressure were recorded. Later, around the turn of the century, a school of Norwegian meteorologists, led by Bjerknes, Solberg, and Bergeron, discovered the importance of air masses in regulating atmospheric movements and therefore in determining the weather. It was learned that there were locations on earth where high and low pressures prevailed, and these were accurately pinpointed. They are sort of factories where good and bad weather are manufactured; technically, one would say that they produce anticyclones and cyclones. As a result, it became possible to publish previsions of increasing accuracy concerning the approach of "warm fronts" or "cold fronts" several days in advance. Meteorological observatories now control a network of stations, permitting them to follow the movements of air masses. Finally, since 1960, it has become possible to forecast the weather on a planetary scale with the help of artificial satellites, which provide the meteorologists with up-to-date maps of the shifting atmospheric air masses over the whole world.

Today meteorology constantly serves airlines, farmers, prospective travelers, and the general public. All of us are concerned with the daily—or hourly—bulletins issued by the meteorological observatories; for a great majority, watching the TV weather report has become a daily ritual. This is not to say that the science of meteorology has completely replaced the recipes of folklore; in many countries, almanacs still publish naive forecasts in which saints or the moon or the planets are used as predictive tools in competition with the science of meteorology.

The Moon and the Rains

As we have seen, the belief that the moon plays a role in controlling the weather is very old and widespread, certainly as old as the Chaldeans. Even today many people contend that the weather changes when the moon does and remains the same until the moon changes again. There is, however, a certain confusion as to the exact nature of the relationship: some attribute to the full moon the effects others claim for the new moon; still others swear by the importance of the first or last quarters. The sheer hoariness of these contradictory opinions has made scientists extremely skeptical of any claims relating the moon to weather conditions. Seventy years ago meteorologists were convinced: their instruments were blind to any lunar influence.

This attitude has changed since then; it now appears that the atmosphere, the sensitive skin that surrounds our planet, is influenced by the moon enough to affect the weather. The effects of the moon are not limited to the tides of the oceans. The same gravitational force that acts on the tides draws away and reshapes the atmosphere at the passage of the moon. At the same time it sends us a whole gamut of electromagnetic waves reflected from the sun. Each month new discoveries are added to the list of the moon's influences on the earth. For instance, it has been found that the moon's position in relation to the sun affects the earth's daily magnetic index. Schulz wrote in 1941:

> Arrhenius was the first to discover the notable effect of the moon on the northern lights and the formation of thunderstorms. Here the maximum takes place when the moon passes through its lowest point in the zodiac. Arrhenius and also, later, Schuster established that a considerably greater number of thunderstorms occur during the waxing phase of the moon than during the waning phase.[1]

The work of Arrhenius may be more valuable as a pioneering effort than as a verified proof, but his ideas did make headway among the specialists, helping them to shed their reluctance to tackle such an ancient hypothesis.

In 1962 Donald A. Bradley and Max A. Woodbury of the University College of Engineering in New York and Glenn W. Brier of the Massachusetts Institute of Technology decided to study the problem in depth. The question they asked was, is there any relationship between the moon and the widespread rainfalls that periodically deluge the continental United States? To find the answer, they enlisted the cooperation of all the 1,544 weather stations that had been in continuous operation over the fifty years from 1900 to 1949. The incidence of widespread rainfalls was plotted against the 29.53 day period of the lunar month, which divides the two new moons and includes the four phases: new moon—first quarter—

full moon—third quarter. Bradley, Woodbury, and Brier found that the incidence of widespread rainfall was distributed irregularly along the lunar month, which suggests that the moon does indeed have an influence on weather:

> It can be stated that, when dates of excessive precipitation are plotted in terms of the angular difference between the moon and sun, a pronounced departure from normal expectancy becomes conspicuous. There is a marked tendency for extreme precipitation in North America to be recorded near the middle of the first and third weeks of the synodical month, especially on the third to fifth days after the configurations of both new and full moon. The second and fourth quarters of the lunation cycle are correspondingly deficient in heavy precipitation, the low point falling about 3 days previous to the date of the alignment of the earth-moon-sun system [see Fig. 1].[2]

Two Australian researchers, E.E. Adderley and E.G. Bowen, of the Radiophysics Division in Sydney, have duplicated these findings in the southern hemisphere: the heaviest rainfall observed by fifty weather stations in New Zealand from 1901 to 1925, plotted in the same way as the U.S. data, was observed to occur during the days immediately following the new and the full moon. This result surprised Adderley and Bowen so much that they did not dare to publish their results until they began a correspondence with the American meteorologists.[3]

In France, Mironovitch and Viart showed in 1958, through painstaking observations, the role played by the moon in certain atmospheric conditions known as "blockages." A blockage develops above a given area when a zone of high pressure prevents a perturbation from leaving. The zone of high pressure forms a wall that forces

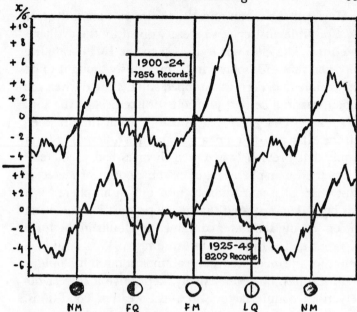

Fig. 1—*The Moon and the Rains*
Between 1900 and 1950, widespread rainfalls recorded by all U.S. weather stations occurred more frequently on days after the new and full moon. The figure shows deviations (in terms of standard measure) of ten-unit moving totals of synodic decimals computed for 16,057 record dates at 1,544 U.S. stations, 1900–49, treated in separate twenty-five year series for correlative comparison. (After Bradley, Woodbury, Brier, *Science,* CXXXVII [1962], 748.)

the bad weather to detour at its sides. The researchers found that during some quarters of the moon the number of blockages increases or decreases depending on the time of the year. For instance, summers in Western Europe from 1945 to 1955 had not one blockage recorded in the period between the first quarter and the full moon.[4] If these works can be confirmed, it will be possible to develop extremely precise meteorological forecasts a long time in advance, since the lunar phases can be predicted by celestial mechanics.

How can the moon affect the rains to such a degree? One possible answer was recently given by the artificial satellites. The clue was found when the IMP-1 satellite reported that the "solar wind," previously thought to be impossible to deflect, was stopped and deflected when the moon was in a certain position with respect to the sun. The energy-charged particles issuing from the sun then hit the earth at a different angle and in a different fashion from what previously accepted theories had predicted.[5] Thus the lunar phases regulate the amount of meteoric dust that falls continuously into our atmosphere.[6,7] It has been demonstrated that meteoric dust has the effect of condensing the water contained in clouds in the form of vapor and is thus able to cause rains. This would account for the moon's effect on abundant rainfall. Popular tradition has, however naively, kept alive a correct observation: cosmic factors do affect weather conditions. Contemporary meteorologists cannot ignore this fact.

The Role of Solar Activity

In the past men conceived the sun to be a perfectly whole sphere—the golden circle of the Pythagoreans. But now we know that the sun is a star in a permanent state of effervescence. It revolves on itself and it is periodically covered with "spots," abrupt explosions of boiling gases that are launched into space with effects that reach down to earth. In this sense one could say that the earth belongs within the radius of the sun's atmosphere: the explosions on the solar surface interfere with the atmospheric electricity of our planet, cause fade-out in radio reception, and account for geomagnetic storms.

These passing perturbations of the sun affect our weather, too. The German H. Berg and the Austrian H.

Hanzlik found in them the explanation for the sudden changes in weather meteorology had been unable to explain before. We refer here to what the experts call "the passage of a warm (or cold) atmospheric front." These "passages" depend on variations of barometric pressure, which change the direction of winds. If the pressure rises, the weather will probably improve; this is called an "anticyclone." If the pressure descends, it is likely that it will rain; this condition is called a "cyclone." It seems that the rise or decline in barometric pressure ultimately depends on the sudden eruptions in the sun. Mustel, the President of the Astronomical Council of the U.S.S.R.'s Academy of Sciences, has collected abundant documentation to show that when the solar surface is active there is a tendency for anticyclones to develop above the land masses and for cyclones to form over the oceans. The weather is then beautiful inland and bad at sea. This rule appears to hold in both hemispheres at the same time.

Is it possible to predict the weather for a given future date, in a specific location, by employing knowledge of the sun's activity? H.C. Willett in the U.S. and Y. Arai in Japan seem to have found affirmative answers. It must be said, however, that at any given place on earth local variables are likely to modify, or to change completely, the general effects of the sun. The relation between the sun and the atmosphere is as complex as that between the two main characters of a psychological novel. There is one more serious stumbling block: the behavior of the sun is completely random from one day to the next. It has been impossible to find any pattern in its daily activity. On the other hand, astronomers have found regular cycles of activity in the sun recurring in longer time periods. If such cycles can be foreseen in advance, will it be possible to develop long-range weather forecasts? The answer seems to be that such an advance is very possible, if the earth's atmosphere is in fact so affected by solar pulsations.

The Study of Tree Rings

The weather marks its imprint on Nature: not only does the sun influence the weather over long periods of time, it also leaves a record of it on earth. Scientists have discovered useful means for establishing the effects of solar activity on the temperature and rainfall, ones that allow them to delve into the past and collect information that can be applied to the prediction of the future. One of these methods is called dendrochronology, or the study of tree rings.

It is well known that the number of rings on a sawed-off tree trunk correspond to the age of the tree in years. But the rings are not the same regardless of conditions: a warm and wet year leaves a wide ring, while a narrow ring is left by a cold and dry season. It is possible in this fashion to reconstruct, by means of the width of tree rings, the climate of the past. The most intriguing aspect of this study is that graphs constructed from tree specimens found in different regions of the globe show an undeniable resemblance to each other, suggesting that there is such a thing as a "climate of the earth." Professor Douglass of the University of Arizona, Director of the Laboratory of Tree Ring Research in Tucson, has studied thousands of tree rings. During his investigations he realized that the earthly climate revealed by the trees followed very closely the rhythm of solar activity. In particular, the eleven-year sun-spot cycle discovered in 1840 by Schwabe was found to be important: the rings of trees all around the world are wider when the number of sun-

spots increases.[8] In the U.S.S.R. Schwedov has duplicated Douglass' studies and found the same periodicity,
signifying that the rains fall more abundantly during
periods of intense solar activity than during periods in
which the sun is quiet.

The Eleven-Year Clocks

The success of dendrochronology has promoted a great
variety of researches aimed at discovering other indica-
tors of weather that follow an eleven-year cycle, under
the timing influence of the sun. A French geophysicist,
Pierre Bernard, has perfected an ingenious method for
discovering which years have the worst meteorological
perturbances. He built extremely sensitive seismographs
that report the faintest movements of the earth crust—
those caused not by earthquakes but by the winds, the
rain, the waves of the sea. After studying the record for
a period of several years, Bernard concluded: "Years in
which micro-seismic tremors are most intense are those
in which there is a sharp decline in solar activity."[9]

Many other related natural phenomena have been
studied. Lury's famous study, *Popular Astronomy*, reported that the number of rabbit furs collected by Hud-
son Bay trappers follows a curve parallel to that of the
sun's activity. Brooks showed the relation of such activity
with the water-level of Lake Victoria in Africa; from
1902 to 1921 the waters rose when the sun was active,
declined when the sun was quiet.[10]* The pattern of sunspots has also been compared with the number of icebergs
and with famines in India due to droughts. According

---

* T. London and M. Haurwitz of the High Altitude Observatory in Boulder, Colorado, have since shown that the correlation
has not been so high in later years.

to the French Astronomical *Bulletin,* years in which the number of sunspots is highest are great vintage years for Burgundy wines; in years with few sunspots poor vintages are produced. The Swiss statistician A. Rima found similar results when he analyzed the production of Rhine wines for the past two hundred years.[11] All these phenomena point to the same cause: the type of weather.

Dating the Past

Another avenue for the study of the earth's past consists in the analysis of varves, which Edward R. Dewey describes as follows:*

> Varves are thin layers of mud laid down year by year. The nature of the material deposited in the winter differs from the material deposited in the summer, so that the varve laid down one year can be distinguished from the varve laid down in the year following. Some varves are thick, others are thin. These differences have been studied under microscopes and have been measured with great accuracy. Varves are usually found in old lake bottoms, many of them in lakes fed by melting glaciers. It stands to reason that in a warm year, when the glaciers melted more, the amount of deposit washed down by the glacier water could be more—and the varve thicker—than in the cool years when the glacier melted less. If this is so, the thickness of the varve should be a rough measure of temperature. Any regularity discovered in the alternate thickness and thinness in the varves would therefore presumptively be a measure of weather cycles.[12]

* The author wishes to thank Edward R. Dewey, Director of the Foundation for the Study of Cycles in East Brady, Pennsylvania, for providing a large number of documents excerpted from his journal, *Cycles.*

The study of these fossil deposits through geological periods has resulted in the measurement of cycles of different lengths. Among them, according to the geologist Zeuner, the eleven-year cycle appears very frequently:

Pre-Cambrian	11.3 years
Superior Devonian	11.4 years
Inferior Carboniferous	11.4 years
Eocene	12.0 years
Oligocene	11.5 years[13]

"Periodicities existed even hundreds of millions of years ago, and thus were the same as today with respect to one of the most important cycles, that of sunspots," writes G. Piccardi, Director of the Institute for Physical Chemistry in Florence, Italy.[14]

A Solar Hand Ticks Off the Centuries

But new facts have been intruding on the scene. Roger Y. Anderson and H.L. Koopmans of the University of New Mexico recently published an article entitled "Harmonic Analysis of Varve Time Series," in which they reported results at some variance with those found by Zeuner. They discovered another, much longer cycle in the sedimentary layers. "The period appears to be near eighty and ninety years and it agrees with the period of the frequency in the spectrum of sunspot numbers, some tree ring spectrums and climatic data."[15]

What could this mean? We have to have a little background before the explanation becomes clear. The classical eleven-year cycle is not the only one. The Swiss astronomer Wolf has discovered pulsations of a much longer amplitude, which are called "secular rhythms" because they lasted almost a century, between eighty and ninety years. For about forty years the sun's activity increases, the eleven-year peaks grow higher and higher. Then the general activity decreases during the next forty years, only to begin growing again. These "secular rhythms" of the sun are reflected not only in the thickness of the varves but in other meteorological phenomena. In 1950 the German botanist F. Schnelle published a report containing some picturesque statistics[16] (*see* Fig. 2). It dealt with the dates of the first annual appearance of snowdrops in the Frankfurt-am-Main region. Snowdrops are small, common flowers that begin to open when the cold weather ends and spring begins. Between 1870 and 1950 the average date for the flowering of snowdrops was February 23. The botanist computed how many days before or after this date the snowdrops first appeared each year. He found a regular curve spanning the eighty years of observation. During the first forty years—from 1870 to 1910—the snowdrops consistently appeared before the average date. But after 1910 they began to flower later and later, attaining the greatest lag in 1925, almost two months behind the average date. Then the snowdrops began to reverse this lag, until now they are again slightly early.

How can the strange behavior of these flowers be explained? Their appearance is of course determined by the rigor and length of the winter. In Germany, when the winds regularly blow from the east, the cold is severe and lasts a long time; the vegetation starts late. The westerly winds, on the other hand, bring a softening of the temperature and, therefore, an earlier spring. The curve of the snowdrops' flowering is an indication that the winds in Germany have followed the same strange cycle. What could be the cause?

The French meteorologist V. Mironovitch thought of

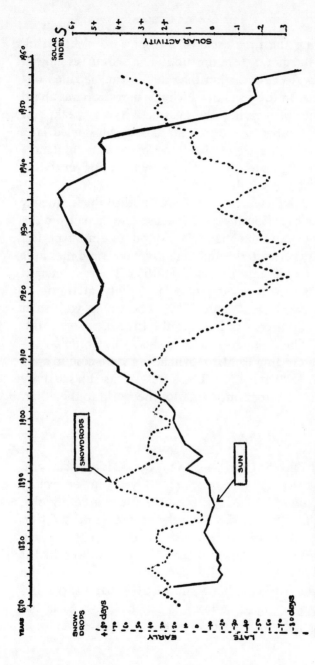

Fig. 2—*Snowdrops and Solar Activity*
Between 1870 and 1960, snowdrops in Germany appeared early when the secular activity of the sun was low (warm winters) and late when the secular activity of the sun was high (harsh winters). (After V. Mironovitch, *Meteorologische Abhandlugen*, IX [1960], 22.)

comparing the time cycle of the snowdrops' flowering
with the secular cycle of the sun.[17] The two curves showed
such a perfect opposition that chance can be ruled out
as a cause. In the years in which the snowdrop was ahead
of its date with spring, the solar activity was weak; and
when the latter was strong, the flowers blossomed late.
Thus the solar cycle of eighty to ninety years influences
the winter temperature in Germany by acting on the direction of the winds.

The Soviet scientist Zhan Ze-Zia studied the frequency
of typhoons in Southwest China, using the data from the
observatory of Shanghai.[18] He found an almost perfect
similarity between the number of typhoons and the curve
of solar activity in the years 1900–1950. The frequency of
typhoons increased with the solar activity, attaining its
peak between 1920 and 1930. The ninety-year solar
rhythms also seem to indicate the time of severe earthquakes. The number of seismic shocks in Chile has followed, according to Mironovitch, the same cosmic cycle
between 1880 and 1960. The effects of the sun's activity
can be traced from one corner of the world to the other.

The Nile and the Saros

In astronomy the nineteen-year period is a crucial one.
About every nineteen years (18.64 years, to be exact),
the sun-moon eclipses occur in the same point of the sky.
When an eclipse darkens the sky on the winter solstice,
nineteen years will pass before the event repeats itself.
This period was known to the Chaldeans, who called it
Saros and believed that its magic powers could cause the
end of the world. Although no scientist shares this belief
nowadays, it would be hasty to conclude that Saros has
nothing to do with what happens on earth. Le Danois, in

a thesis that was very popular for some time, emphasized the great importance that Saros can have on our lives. He claimed that the combined gravitational pull of the sun and the moon acts on the tides, causing widespread disturbances in bodies of water. These currents, which flow across the oceans, may account for the changes in climate during the centuries. Even if his argument was carried a little too far, a recent study by another hydraulic engineer, Paris-Teynac, shows a similar pattern for several large rivers, and especially for the Nile—the cradle of Egyptian civilization.

Data on the tides of the Nile are available as far back as four thousand years. The pharaoh, worshiped as the "master of the growth of waters," attached a great importance to exactly how much water there would be in the river each year, for it brought wealth and nourishment to his people. The records that were kept almost uninterruptedly up to our days allowed Prince Omar Toussoun to reconstruct the Nile's biography over several thousand years. Some strange facts about rivers emerge from these records. The great Egyptian river has followed clear rhythmic variations that approximate certain astronomical cycles. Paris-Teynac has identified an eleven-year variation that seems to be tied to the sunspot cycle. Above all, he has shown eighteen-year periods, roughly corresponding to the Saros, which reflect the sun-moon eclipse intervals. "It is possible," he says, "that the Saros, which the Chaldeans believed to be so important, increases the water-level in some parts of the world."[19] It would be helpful if these first results could be checked against a study of the other large African rivers, such as the Senegal or the Niger. Unfortunately, their written history is not as long as the Nile's. The Egyptians, who did not know where the sources of the Nile were, assumed that its bounty descended directly from heaven. In his hymn to the sun god, the pharaoh Ikhnaton wrote 3,500 years ago: "You have given us a Nile in heaven, so that it can descend on us." To be sure, it was only a dream; but the work of contemporary scientists shows that the movement of major rivers may be dependent on celestial motions.

The Planets and Ice Ages

Delving even further into the past, some researchers have attempted to relate the gravitational influence of the planets to the ice ages that have alternated over our globe. Each planet in the solar system affects the earth's movement by its gravity. These effects are, of course, quite slight compared with those of the sun or the moon. But they do cause changes in the eccentricity and the inclination of the earth's orbit. Such changes are extremely slow, and they can be computed for a hundred thousand years in the past and predicted for a hundred thousand years in the future. It is not impossible that they might have had a deep effect on our climate. The Serbian astronomer M. Milankovitch, in 1938, tried to use them to explain the succession of glacial epochs. The climatic curves Milankovitch calculated correspond rather amazingly to the curves of glacial advances. The same curves also follow the cycles of temperature change in the oceans during the same geological period published by Hans Suess of the University of California, in 1956.

Some scientists cast doubt on Milankovitch's figures. But they do this only to advance other cosmic explanations; for instance, E.J. Opik of the University of Maryland believes that solar pulsations lasting several thousand years are responsible for the cooling and the

warming of the earth.[20] Other specialists have come to
the Serbian scientist's defense. George Gamov, from the
University of Colorado, has written in this respect:

> Despite the objections of some climatologists, who
> claim that a few degrees' difference in temperature
> could not have caused the glacial periods, it seems that
> the old Serbian was right. Therefore we have to con-
> clude that, although the planets are without influence
> on the lives of individuals (as the astrologers would
> have it), they certainly affect the life of men, animals,
> and plants through the long geological periods.[21]

The Planets and Radio Reception

In 1951 John H. Nelson, propagation analyst at RCA
Communications, was put in charge of a study involving
the quality of the reception of radio broadcasts. It had
been known for some time that the quality of reception
depends on sunspot activity, and especially on the passage of the larger spots across the meridian. When solar
activity was correlated with ease of reception, a con-
spicuous variance remained unaccounted for. Nelson
thought that this residue could be explained in terms of
the heliocentric position of the planets, that is, their position as related to the sun. After many observations, he
concluded:

> The research conducted at this observatory since 1946
> has quite definitely indicated that sunspots themselves
> are not the full answer to the problems that are mani-
> fest. There is very strong evidence that some other
> forces are at work in addition to the sunspots. The need
> of a new approach is indicated. The study of the planets
> as a new approach to propagation analysis has netted
> encouraging results and shows sufficient promise to war-

rant further and deeper study. A highly developed fore-casting technique of this type would enable forecasting to be done several years ahead since advance plane-tary phenomena can be calculated with very great accuracy.[22]

According to Nelson, certain specific planetary config-urations cause disturbances in radio reception: those in which, in relation to the sun, the planets find themselves either at right angles to each other, or in conjunction, or in opposition. In 1963, J.A. Roberts wrote an article in *Planetary Space Science Research* showing that Venus, Jupiter, and Saturn are the source of powerful radio waves received by the earth.[23] In 1966, reporting to the Academy of Sciences in Paris, the astronomer Michel Trellis showed evidence that the gravitational effect of the planets modulates the eleven-year solar activity cycle.[24] Similar works have been published lately in the U.S., in the U.S.S.R., and in Germany. "Since it has been demonstrated that the planets can affect the sun, one must admit the possibility that they may affect the earth, which is closer to them than the sun is," wrote the chemist G. Piccardi.[25] Among American scientists, E.K. Bigg pro-poses that Venus and Mercury have an effect on the mag-netic storms blowing on the earth.[26] Atkinson has col-lected statistics showing the similar role of the moon and of Mars.[27]

These and similar observations are still difficult to ex-plain. But in the last ten years, artificial satellites have revolutionized our conceptions of space. The strange ef-fects of the moon and of the planets may be due to the extremely long wakes they leave behind them, known by the specialists as "magnetospheric tails." In 1964, A.T. Dessler calculated that the length of the earth's magneto-spheric tail was at least twenty times the distance between the earth and the moon. According to Bowen, the magnetospheric tails of the other planets extend the same distance in space.[28] Astrophysicists nowadays tend to think more and more that interplanetary space is not empty, as it was believed to be fifty years ago, but that it is traversed by a great number of forces, many of which have not yet been observed. Buffeted by these forces, the sun especially, but also the moon and the planets, brings about the forces and disturbances that reverberate on the earth.

The Earth as a Clock

The best clock we know of is the earth itself: it turns on its axis in twenty-three hours and fifty-six minutes without fail. This period is called the sidereal day. Astronomers chose it as the unit for the measurement of time because they thought that its unvarying rhythm would never change. Only recently, with the availability of instruments of incredible precision, have they discovered that the length of the earth's rotation is variable. The sidereal day is sometimes longer, sometimes shorter: the difference never exceeds a few milliseconds, but the fact is that not even the earth keeps perfect time. As a consequence of this discovery sidereal time was abandoned as the basic unit of time. To find the more precise timekeeper technical progress needs, the specialists had to turn to the tiny intervals that separate atomic reactions. The atom has replaced the earth as a clock.

But what causes the erratic performance of this old-fashioned pendulum? The astronomers, using atomic clocks, found the cause in the cosmos; tied to the sun as they both hurl in space, the earth is buffeted from each angle by cosmic forces. Every neighboring celestial body has some effect on it. The moon, through the tides, increases the length of the days by imperceptible increments. The sudden eruptions of the sun also affect the earth's rotation, and so can all the other planets, in principle. All these effects are mere infinitesimal fractions of a second, but the phenomenon is nevertheless impressive, considering how much energy is needed to "reset" a mass the size of the earth. And if the earth can be jostled at the caprice of space, what happens to man, an insignificantly small organism living on its surface, when the cosmic forces are unleashed?

NOTES TO CHAPTER SEVEN

1. F. Schulz, *Bio-Dynamics,* Winter, 1941; *Cycles,* X (1959), No. 9, 201.
2. D. Bradley, M. Woodbury, and G. Brier, "Lunar Synodical Period and Widespread Precipitation," *Science,* CXXXVII (1962), 748.
3. E. Adderley and E. Bowen, "Lunar Component in Precipitation Data," *Science,* CXXXVII (1962), 749.
4. V. Mironovitch and R. Viart, "Interruption du courant zonal en Europe Occidentale et sa liaison avec l'activité solaire," *Meteorologische Abhandlungen,* Vol. VII (1958), No. 3.
5. National Aeronautics and Space Administration, *Initial Results of the I.M.P.-1 Magnetic Field Experiment* (Greenbelt, Maryland: Goddard Space Flight Center, April, 1964).
6. E.G. Bowen, "A Lunar Effect on the Incoming Meteor Rate," *Journal of Geophysical Research,* LXVIII (1963), No. 5, 1401.
7. D. Brierley and J. Davies, "Lunar Influence on Meteor Rates," *Journal of Geophysical Research,* LXVIII (1963), No. 22, 6213.
8. A. Boischot, *Le soleil et la terre* (Paris: P.U.F., 1966).
9. P. Bernard, "Le cycle solaire dans l'agitation microséismique," *C.R.A.S.,* CCVI (1938), 1585.
10. C. Brooks, "Variation in the Levels of the Central African Lakes Victoria," *Geophysical Memoirs,* No. 20 (London: Meteorological Office, 1923).
11. A. Rima, "Considerazioni su una serie agraria bisecolare: la produzione di vino ne Rheingau 1719–1950," *Geofis. e Meteor,* XII (1963), 29.
12. E.R. Dewey, "Cycle Timing Varies with Latitude," *Cycles,* IX (1958), No. 11, 288.
13. F.E. Zeuner, *Dating the Past* (London: Methuen, 1950).
14. G. Piccardi, *The Chemical Basis of Medical Climatology* (Springfield, Ill.: Charles Thomas, 1962).
15. R. Anderson and H. Koopmans, "Harmonic Analysis of Varve Time Series," *Journal of Physical Research,* LXVIII (1963), No. 3, 877.

16. F. Schnelle, "Hundert Jahre phänologische Beobachtungen im Rhein-Main Gebiet," *Meteor. Rundschau*, 7/8, 1950.

17. V. Mironovitch, "Sur l'évolution séculaire de l'activité solaire et ses liaisons avec la circulation générale," *Meteor. Abhandlungen*, IX (1960), No. 3.

18. Zhan Ze-Zia, *Meteo. i Hydrol.*, Leningrad, No. 11, p. 24, 1958.

19. E. Paris-Teynac, "Contribution à la connaissance des fleuves d'Afrique Tropicale et en particulier le Nil," *Bull. I. F. A. N.*, XXV (1963), 1.

20. E.J. Opik, "Climatic Change in Cosmic Perspective," *Icarus*, IV (1965), 289.

21. G. Gamov, *La gravitation* (Paris: Payot, 1962).

22. J.H. Nelson, "Shortwave Radio Propagation Correlation with Planetary Positions," *R.C.A. Review*, XII (1951), No. 1, 26.

23. J.A. Roberts, "Radio Emission from the Planets," *Planetary Space Science Research*, XI (1963), No. 3, 221.

24. M. Trellis, "Sur une relation possible entre l'aire des taches solaires et la position des planètes," *C.R.A.S.*, CCLXII (1966), 312.

25. M. Gauquelin, *L'hérédité planétaire*, with a preface by Professor G. Piccardi (Paris: Planète, 1966).

26. E.K. Bigg, "Lunar and Planetary Influences on Geomagnetic Disturbances," *Journal of Geophysical Research*, LXVIII (1963), 4099.

27. G. Atkinson, "Planetary Effects on Magnetic Activity," *Trans. Amer. Geophys. Un.*, XLV (1964), No. 4, 630.

28. E.G. Bowen, "Lunar and Planetary Tails in the Solar Wind," *Journal of Geophysical Research*, LXIX (1964), 4969.

Mysterious Rhythms

Oₙₑ ₒf ₜₕₑ ᵦₐₛᵢ꜀ and most mysterious properties of life is its dependence on rhythms. Different
rhythms have been found to regulate everything, not only
the life of animals but also that of plants, not only the
organism as a whole but each of the separate organs, every
cell, and the swirling atoms of which it is made. Rhythmic pulses underlie all biological reactions, from the
most elementary cellular processes to those of the organism as a whole. When seen more closely, the movement
of such rhythms appears to be the effect of real "biological clocks" that keep time for the whole of life. Pro-
toplasm has the remarkable ability to structure time into
regular periods. This does not surprise us in certain familiar instances, such as the rhythms of breathing, heart-
beat, or spasmodic nervous discharges. But how are the
other thousand-and-one clocks ticking away in nature
regulated?

The Need for Rhythms

For all living things, whatever their level of organization, the rhythm is as basic as life itself. The "loss of a

beat" is always dangerous for the organism; its essential functions become disorganized. If the rhythm is not found again quickly, the organism may not survive. Moreover, an organism cannot live if the rhythm of another organism out of phase with that of the first is artificially imposed on it. That the alien rhythm acts as a fatal poison has been shown by the recent experiments performed on the common cockroach by the biologist Janet Harker of Cambridge University.[1] As a result of extremely ingenious surgical operations, she has found that "a gland in the head of cockroaches secretes a hormone associated with, and at least partially responsible for, the onset of activity in these creatures."[2] If the gland of a normally active cockroach is transferred to a cockroach whose activity has been arrested for a long period through exposure to constant light, the second cockroach will begin to live on the rhythm of the first, whose gland now directs its behavior. Does the insect survive the intrusion of a foreign rhythm into its cells? It depends:

> When some suboesophagial ganglion glands from cockroaches with activity set to normal time of day are transplanted into cockroaches whose clocks were also set to the normal time of day, the host cockroaches all remain healthy. Where glands from cockroaches with activity set to normal time of day are transplanted into cockroaches whose regulatory clocks have been reset by inverted light cycles, the host cockroaches all die with intestinal cancer.[3]

Survival requires that the different rhythms of our body be synchronized; if they fail to keep time with each other they cause an illness as serious as the lesion of a specific organ would be.

A Classification of Rhythms

It has been known for a long time that physiological rhythms tend to follow the lead of the environment. Sometimes they adapt themselves to the periods defined by the earth's motions or its position in space. The three main environmental rhythms are: the daily rhythm, which depends on the earth's turning on itself every twenty-four hours; the monthly rhythm of the moon's turning around the earth; and the yearly rhythm of the earth's turning around the sun. These are the three basic timegivers of life.

Organisms are able to follow an environmental rhythm by perceiving the rhythm's by-products, changes in light, temperature, humidity, etc. All living organisms are sensitive to these changes. The effects of the yearly rhythm are familiar to everyone: in spring the increase in temperature causes the blossoms to open and the animals to begin their courtship. At winter's approach the cold curtails activity: trees shed their foliage and animals hide in their lairs to hibernate.

The daily rhythm is equally obvious. Most plants and animals follow a twenty-four-hour cycle of sleep and wakefulness. But there are many variations on this basic pattern. The butterfly is set on the light of day, while the cat and the owl are adapted to use the darkness. Plants use sunlight as a source of energy, and actively synthesize their nourishment during the day. Flowers open up with the light and close their petals in the evening—but here, too, there are exceptions. There is, for example, the *Selenicereus grandiflorus*, whose large white flowers open about midnight. The twenty-four-hour rhythm, without doubt the most important one affecting earthly life, has been intensively studied by specialists. One of them, F. Halberg, says that this rhythm is an adaptation in the time-dimension "as basic as cellular structural organization in space."[4] Sometimes the daily and yearly rhythms complement each other, producing cycles of exquisite sensitivity in certain animal species. For instance, the bean aphid can either give birth to live offspring or lay eggs, depending on the time of the year, and the length of the day on which the offspring are born determines the transition from one of these modes of reproduction to the other. Professor Anthony D. Lees of Cambridge has observed that when daylight lasts longer than fourteen hours and fifty-five minutes, the offspring is born alive. If the day is shorter by even a few minutes, the offspring is born inside an egg that will hatch later. Inside the female bean aphid's body is an extremely delicate "clock" that works as a mathematical time-memory of infinite precision.

Astonishing Complexities

The reproductive cycles of many sea animals are based on rhythms connected with the movement of the tides. The rising of the tide depends on the respective position of the sun and of the moon; when they are in conjunction or in opposition, their gravitational effect becomes additive, producing much stronger tides than the ones that occur when the sun and the moon are at right angles to each other as seen from the earth. This rhythm rules certain wonderfully complex biological clocks. Here is how Rachel Carson describes the extraordinary behavior of the grunion:

> No other creature displays so exquisite an adaptation to the tidal rhythm as the grunion—a small, shimmer-

ing fish about as long as a man's hand. Through no one can say what processes of adaptation, extending over no one knows how many millennia, the grunion has come to know not only the daily rhythm of the tides, but the monthly cycle by which certain tides sweep higher on the beaches than others. It has so adapted its spawning habits to the tidal cycle, that the very existence of the race depends on the precision of this adjustment.

Shortly after the full moon of the months from March to August, the grunion appear in the surf on the beaches of California. The tide reaches flood stage, slackens, hesitates, and begins to ebb. Now on these waves of the ebbing tide the fish begin to come in. Their bodies shimmer in the light of the moon as they are borne up the beach on the crest of a wave, they lie glittering on the wet sand for a perceptible moment of time, then fling themselves into the wash of the next wave and are carried back to sea. For about an hour after the turn of the tide this continues, thousands upon thousands of grunion coming up onto the beach, leaving the water, returning to it. This is the spawning act of the species.

During the brief interval between successive waves, the male and female have come together in the wet sand, the one to shed her eggs, the other to fertilize them. When the parent fish return to the water, they have left behind a mass of eggs buried in the sand. Succeeding waves on that night do not wash out the eggs because the tide is already ebbing. The waves of the next high tide will not reach them, because for a time after the full moon each tide will halt its advance a little lower on the beach than the preceding one. The eggs, then, will be undisturbed for at least a fortnight. In the warm, damp, incubating sand they undergo their development. Within two weeks the magic change from fertilized egg to larval fishlet is completed, the perfectly formed little grunion still confined within the membranes of the egg, still buried in the sand, waiting for release. With the tides of the new moon it. comes. Their waves wash over the places where the little masses of the grunion eggs were buried, the swirl and rush of the surf stirring the sand deeply. As the sand is washed away, and the eggs feel the touch of the cool sea water, the membranes rupture, the fishlets hatch, and the waves that released them bear them away to the sea.[5]

Among marine species the grunion is not an exception. The same complex, finely tuned behavior is found in several other living things. The brown seaweed *Dictyota*, for instance, follows the moon very closely. A physiologist at the University of Tübingen, E. Bünning, summarizes this relationship as follows: "The maximum discharge of eggs takes place nine days after exposure to the moonlight. The next maximum then follows after an interval of 15 to 16 days."[6] This periodicity is similar in length to half a lunar cycle. The intensity of the moon's light in this case acts as a timer. It is amazing how faint a glimmer synchronizes the "physiological lunar rhythm" of this seaweed; as Bünning points out, the light of the moon is three hundred thousand times less than that of the sun.[7] That the survival of an apparently blind plant should depend on such infinitesimal lighting changes suggests that living organisms will take enormous pains to set their timing to the most minute cosmic stimuli.

Unintelligible Behaviors

There is an ancient tradition among Mediterranean fishermen according to which edible marine animals such as sea urchins, clams, and oysters are "full" when the moon is full, and "empty" at the new moon. Although this belief has not always been supported by scientific observation, it has been shown to be true, at least in the case of a sea urchin of the Red Sea, *Centrechinus cetosus:*

> During the good season—end of July to September—at the full moon the genital substance is released in the sea, to permit fecundation. After this event, the size of the ovaries and testes decreases. Then the production of gonadic cells begins again, progresses through the new moon, and reaches its maximum at the full moon when the ova and the spermatozoa are mature.[8]

The lunar rhythm of *Centrechinus cetosus* is difficult to explain; the strength of the tides cannot account for it, as in the case of grunion, since tides are almost nonexistent in the Red Sea.

The spectacular behavior of several sea worms also remains unexplained:

> In Bermuda, at the time of full moon in April, May and June, the Atlantic fireworm swarms in its breeding rhythm a few minutes after sunset. At this time, the females emerge from their coral hideouts, swim to the surface, and become brilliantly luminous. The males are apparently attracted by the light, and breeding takes place in the water. A comparable reproductive rhythm in Bermuda waters has been described for the shrimp *Anchistioides*, which swarms just before midnight two or three days before, and two or three days after, new moon.[9]

Another worm whose behavior is quite remarkable is the one called Palolo, or *Leodice viridix*, whose habitat is in the coral reefs of the Pacific. During the months of October and November, when the moon is in the last quarter, the back half of the worm, filled with genital matter, separates itself from the front half. While the anterior half remains on the reef and dies, the genital section rises to the surface of the sea like the last stage of a rocket, and there it spreads its contents. The eggs and spermatozoa are thus allowed to mix at low tide, for several days at a time. So many worms are involved in this reproductive process that the sea seems to change its color; during this period the Samoans celebrate one of their great holidays, for they find the fried meat of the worm a great delicacy.

These are only a few examples that show that strange rhythms do in fact exist in the animal and vegetal kingdoms, rhythms that are related to certain cosmic factors involving the sun and the moon.

Toward A Simple Explanation

Specialists have recognized the amazing precision of the biological clocks for some time, but until a few years ago they contended that the causes were not as mysterious as they appeared at first glance. Scientists believed that they knew all the factors involved: the intensity of sunlight, for instance, was responsible for the birth of the bean aphid; the intensity of moonlight regulated the behavior of the alga *Dictyota;* in addition, humidity, temperature, and the strength of tides were supposed to control the reproductive rhythms of plants and animals; finally, the atmospheric pressure was held responsible for exerting a deep influence over animal behavior.

These beliefs could be tested by laboratory experiments. All one had to do was to place some sensitive organisms in an environment in which the natural schedules of light, temperature, humidity, and pressure were slowly modified; as a consequence, the rhythms dependent on these factors would also slowly change until they adapted themselves to the artificial schedule. These experiments have been performed. The rhythm of the known physical factors in the environment has been modified, and the corresponding change in the animal's behavior has been observed. Most of the results obtained in varying light intensity have been as expected. Daylight alone is a powerful timer. But not all the experiments were equally satisfying; in fact, the complacent assurance of scientists was severely jolted. What findings were responsible for such a change?

Professor Frank A. Brown became involved in a study of *Uca pugnax*, or fiddler crab, whose name derives from its huge pincer's resemblance to a violin. One characteristic of this animal is that its color is darkest at noon, and clearest at midnight. In a series of laboratory experiments, Brown produced an inversion of the twenty-four-hour cycle, so that the period of light in the laboratory corresponded to darkness outside, and vice-versa. As expected, the color-cycle of the crab adapted itself to the new pattern. However, when as a result of further experiments the fiddler crabs were placed in a great variety of other environmental conditions, a surprising result emerged: no matter how varied and extreme the changes in the laboratory, the biological clock of the crab kept time with itself, maintaining the same rhythm of color change despite everything. Heat or cold had no effect: crabs brought up at 47 and at 80 degrees Fahrenheit kept to exactly the same rhythm. In later experiments Brown resorted to poisons—cyanide, as an example—to observe the effects of metabolic paralysis. This permitted the experimenter to affect organisms to the point of almost completely arresting their functioning. It was found that even while the rest of the bodily functions were completely paralyzed, the performance of the biological clocks remained almost totally unaffected. Brown concluded: "In short, the clock exhibits fantastic immunities to chemicals which influence metabolic changes, and to temperature changes."[10]

Analogous behavior was observed in experiments conducted with dry seeds. It was shown by Bünning that if one keeps dry grain seed in a container at uniform temperature, and then extracts samples from time to time, the percentage of seed that will germinate depends on the season of the year. This is astonishing, because the seeds are very dry and therefore in a state of almost arrested life: how could they be aware what part of the year it was when they were taken out of the container? And this is not all; when the seed was kept at extreme temperatures ranging from 40 degrees below freezing to 110 Fahrenheit, its extraordinary sensitivity to seasonal changes was not impaired.

Is the Clock Internal?

Confronted with such intriguing behavior, scientists assumed that living organisms possess an internal clock of a chemical nature. This would result in a simple explanation of the otherwise disturbing findings. Bünning, for instance, held the opinion that seed contains in its cells a genetically inherited "memory clock," which is practically impervious to everything in the environment. Thus the rhythms of living organisms would be caused by internal factors or, in the language of the specialists, would be endogenous in nature.

Professor Brown describes the above position as follows:

> The organism is a wholly self-contained clock-system, as for example a good calendar wrist watch with timer

built in. Dr. Colin Pittendrigh and Dr. Victor Bruce of Princeton University postulate that the basic timers of the clock system are naturally oscillating physico-chemical systems inside the organism itself; the oscillations continue independently of all rhythmic changes in the organism's environment. The length of the periods of these systems are considered inherited and their coincidence with the natural geophysical periods reflects adaptation to the conditions of our planet over the course of millions of years.[11]

According to this theory, the role of changing cosmic environments is reduced to a bare minimum. For quite a long time, the great majority of specialists who studied biological rhythms accepted this explanation. Even today, most of them believe that endogenous factors are the only rational cause of the stubborn behavior of living clocks.

Facts That Contradict the Theory •

Nevertheless, some statistics that could not fit into this explanatory framework did exist. Among the troublesome findings were those resulting from the work of Dr. Burr at Yale, who studied variations in the electrical potential of trees by drilling two holes in the trunk of a tree and inserting one end of a piece of wire in each hole. An electric current flowed along the wire, but the voltage varied and the current flowed sometimes one way, sometimes the other. Dr. Burr noticed that the changes in the potential of trees followed a cycle tuned in with cosmic cycles: "Of all the external factors examined, the phase of the moon seems to be the only one showing any degree of correlation." Yet the sun also appears to have a role: "There is a striking relationship between the changing sunspot activity, on the one hand, and the potentials on the other."[12]

It is as if the tree contained an electrical decoder capable of "guessing" the action of cosmic factors. Such behavior is difficult to reconcile in terms of an internal rhythm theory. Nor is it easy to see how the theory can explain the findings of the Soviet entomologist Stcherbinovsky. After recording the migration pattern of locusts on a map of the world for forty years, he found a relationship between the dispersion of the insects and the eleven-year activity of sunspots.[13] His compatriot Derjavin observed that the same solar rhythm coincides with changes in the reproduction and death ratios of sturgeons in the Caspian Sea. On the shores of Lake Victoria, where tides are absent, Hartland-Rowe in 1958 and MacDonald in 1956 observed rhythmic patterns in the development of various insects.[14, 15] These rhythms were connected with the phases of the moon, for no obvious reason. There is a parallel finding in regard to the striping of a certain genus of corals called *Flabellum*. The striations are an index of their progressive growth. While the yearly cycle of strips is easy to explain, it is more difficult to find a cause for the monthly and daily striations:

> The monthly striping is perhaps due to a reproductive periodicity tied to the lunar cycle, which has already been found in other corals. As for the third-order stripings (the daily increments), they do not seem to follow the tides, and their explication appears to depend on the daily variation of light.[16]

But the problem is that "there are varieties of the same coral which live at great depths, where the sunlight fails to penetrate. It has been observed that these corals also show three orders of striping. How can this phenomenon be explained?"[17] The question is, how can the coral keep to its rhythm at a depth where the *external conditions remain uniform* and neither tides nor light can affect its growth?

The Possibility of Exogenous Rhythms

The state of knowledge in the field was rather confused until Brown delivered a substantial clarification. His success was due to the fact that instead of looking at the above-mentioned observations as troublesome exceptions, he viewed them as examples of a positive law. There was evidence of many contradictions in the doctine of "endogenous rhythms." One had the choice of dismissing the contradictions as irrelevant, or of using them as a departure for a new interpretation. Brown chose the latter approach, and had a remarkable idea: to study the behavior of organisms in perfectly uniform environmental conditions. He attempted to keep experimental animals in the same temperature, humidity, pressure, and so on for as long as possible. In other words, Brown decided to create a condition exactly opposite to what had been tried before: instead of varying the environment as much as possible, he would reduce variation completely. If the supporters of the "endogenous rhythms" theory were right, under conditions of reduced variation nothing special would happen; the internal clocks would continue to follow their millenary schedule.

Brown began his experiments in 1946; ever since, his discoveries have been chipping away at the assurance of those who believe in internal clocks. Under carefully controlled conditions, the biological clocks present incomprehensible variations. Deprived of their habitual "obvious rhythms," plants and animals display behavior indicating that they are under the rule of new, hitherto unnoticed cosmic rhythms. Confined in their dungeons, the organisms are still receiving outside messages. They are constantly aware of certain modifications in the geophysical environment—as if spies were able to slip messages into the rigidity of "uniform conditions."

Clocks Two Days Fast

One of Brown's experiments consisted in placing potatoes, carrots, and salamanders in containers and measuring the metabolic activity of these organisms as revealed by the quantity of oxygen released, using a clever method he himself developed. Despite the highly unusual conditions under which the organisms were placed, the curve of their "oxygen consumption" displayed some characteristic correspondences to the curve of barometric pressure reported outside the laboratory two days *after* each measurement. Not only were the biological clocks modified by the changed conditions, the modifications appeared to be tied to future external conditions. "In fact," Brown writes, "every living thing studied in our laboratory during the past three years—from carrots to seaweed, and from crabs and oysters to rats—has shown this capacity to predict very safely beyond chances the barometric pressure change usually two days in advance."[18]

Brown made further discoveries with the same and other experimental subjects. Three years of continuous observation of potatoes have shown that metabolic activity follows a daily pattern consisting of three consumption peaks, one near sunrise, the second at noon, and the third near sunset. Yet variations in light, temperature, or humidity cannot account for these peaks, since all three were held constant in the laboratory. A similar mystery applies to Brown's findings in relation to the lunar day. It appears that potatoes, algae, carrots, earthworms, and salamanders all "know" where the moon is, whether it has just appeared over the horizon, whether it is at the zenith, or whether it is setting. "The similarity of changes such as these in metabolic rate with the time of lunar day can be plausibly explained only by saying that all are responding to a common external physical fluctuation having a lunar period," comments Brown[19] (*see* Fig. 3).

Oysters and the Moon's Time

These were only the beginnings of Professor Brown's discoveries. With a team of assistants including, among others, Webb, Bennett, Terracini, Barnwell, all of Northwestern University, he decided to attack the problem in an even more original way. What would happen, they asked, if the animals were left under uniform conditions but the cosmic factors were varied? To answer the question, Brown had some live oysters sent in closed, darkened containers from Long Island Sound to his laboratory in Evanston, a thousand miles from the sea. When they arrived, he observed their activity by measuring the opening of their valves. At first the oysters kept to their natural rhythm, opening and closing themselves to the rhythm of the tides washing Long Island Sound. But after about fifteen days Brown noticed that a slippage in the daily rhythm had occurred. The oysters now opened up *at the time the tide would have flooded Evanston, had the town been on the seashore*—that is, when the moon passed over the local meridian. The oysters had abandoned their rhythm tied to actual tides, and responded to an exclusively lunar rhythm. They were "reset" by an unknown influence related to the passage of the moon

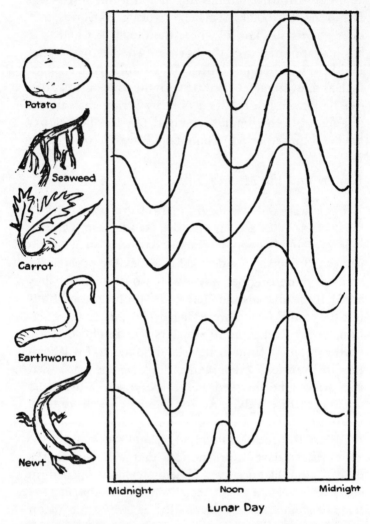

Midnight   Noon   Midnight

Lunar Day

Fig. 3—*The "Lunatic" Life*
Plants and animals are mysteriously aware of the moon's location in the sky. Their metabolic activity, measured by oxygen consumption, depends on the lunar day even when they are unable to see the moon. (After F. A. Brown, Jr., *Biological Clocks* [Boston: American Institute of Biological Sciences, 1962], p. 20.)

above the meridian of Evanston—all this while they were shielded in the dark tanks of the laboratory.[20]

A Surprising Activity

The next question Brown asked was, how would animals react to similar conditions? In 1959 he and Terracini demonstrated that rats too respond to the movements of the moon. A rat was kept for months in a closed cage with constant light, temperature, and pressure. There was no way for the rat to know whether it was night or day, whether the moon was above or below the horizon. When Brown and Terracini recorded the rat's physical activity, they found clear peaks in activity corresponding to the moon's position: the rat was more active during the hours in which the moon was below the horizon, and quietest when it was above the horizon. It moved six times as much during the first hour of the lunar day as during the eleventh. This lunar periodicity was complemented by a sub-pattern, which seemed to depend on the sun's movements.[21] The above experiment has been duplicated and confirmed; a 1962 study on mice also shed new light on the issues involved.

It has also been found that animals are sometimes caught between the rhythm of the sun and that of the moon, even though they are sheltered from the apparent effect of both these celestial bodies. This discovery was made while Brown was recording the activity of hamsters during an eight-month period in 1965. At first the rodents synchronized their activity with the rising and the setting of the sun, which was probably their natural rhythm before they had been confined to their cages. Then, suddenly, the twenty-four-hour rhythm changed to a new, slightly longer rhythm, one that lasted twenty-four hours and fifty minutes. This period corresponds exactly to the length of a lunar day, since the moon always rises fifty minutes later each day in relation to the sun. But the new rhythm did not remain constant; sometimes the hamsters would go back to the twenty-four-hour rhythm of the solar day. Their pattern of activity switched throughout the study, first following one and then the other of the two celestial bodies—without their ever knowing the position of either, in the darkness of their experimental lodgings.[22]

Genetic Knowledge

We will cite one last experiment published by one of Brown's collaborators.[23] Fertilized hen's eggs were placed inside an incubator, and the breathing of the embryos was checked. During the first five days of incubation the embryos showed an average twenty-four-hour variation with peaks related to sunrise, moon, and sunset, just as potatoes had. The embryos appeared to be aware of when the sun rose and set, despite the uniform lighting and temperature of their sealed environment. When after a week the chicks had developed their capacity for muscular activity, the breathing apparatus showed that their activity increased when the sun rose and declined when the sun set, in keeping with their inherited diurnal nature. Obviously, the embryo had never seen the sun; yet a "genetic knowledge" of these celestial bodies' movements manifests itself as soon as the embryos are old enough to react to it in a coordinated manner. By what unimagined ways does this knowledge filter through the shell and reach the tiny organism huddling inside it? We recognize here an old question posed anew. Again, an answer invoking purely internal rhythms seems insufficient. There is, of course, an endogenous mechanism that allows organic reactions to occur. But the initial condition, the factor that accounts for the timing of the hands on the biological clock, seems to reside far away, in the movements of the cosmos.

A Sacrilegious Hypothesis

Accumulating facts of this nature suggested to Brown a hypothesis that, as he put it himself, was rather sacrilegious. It brought down thunderbolts from the Olympus of science on the head of its creator. What he suggested, in short, was that the uniform environmental conditions of the laboratory were not so uniform as had previously been thought: there were some unknown factors originating in space that laboratory conditions could not control; their effect was to "reset the organism to cosmic time." When the crabs or the oysters, for instance, change their cycle of activity to conform with the "upper and lower transits of the moon, the only plausible explanation is that these creatures are obtaining information as to the moon's position through some subtle channels," writes Brown.[24] He offers an explanation for the existence of biological clocks that runs counter to previously existing theories: *the rhythms are external,* imposed upon the organism by the cosmic and geophysic environment. To use his own simile:

> The second of the two possibilities for the basic timer is that the organism is more to be compared with the ordinary electric clock, which is really no clock at all in one sense, since it has no built-in timer. It has instead a synchronous motor that permits it to count the 60-cycle-per-second electric oscillations generated by the power plant, and measure time with this information. In other

words, according to this second hypothesis, the various clocks within the organism are timed by the common rhythmic geophysical environment of this planet.[25]

In an article in *Science*, in 1959, he refined this thought as follows:

> During the past six years the rapidly mounting evidence for a most unorthodox, and even a most incredible, character of any fully autonomous internal clock in terms of our current knowledge of general physiology rendered it advisable to reconsider the working hypothesis of an independent or "closed system" clock.

The hypothesis that appears most credible in light of such evidence, he adds, "is the hypothesis that the clock comprises an 'open system' and that timing of the periods persisting in so-called constant conditions is derived through a continuous response of the living organism to its rhythmic geophysical environment."[26]

It was indeed incredible to assume that influences coming from space could penetrate to the interiors of laboratories, to disrupt the most carefully controlled experimental conditions! In fact, its formulation provoked an intense debate in scientific circles. It was to be expected that scientists who had developed a theory of endogenous rhythms based on so many ingenious experiments would not easily be convinced of the importance of exogenous rhythms. The discussion, while always polite, was nevertheless quite impassioned and contained a certain dosage of humor; one can mention in this context the warnings that L.C. Cole has given to his colleagues against the inconsiderate use of numbers. Cole proved that statistics can be made to show anything; he succeeded in discovering the "exogenous rhythm" of the unicorn! There is no doubt, he concluded, that some so-called exogenous rhythms are as imaginary as the unicorn itself.[27]

In conclusion, we are faced with a basic question: What are these unknown forces to which animals and plants react so readily? Can they be clarified? And does not one have to assume a fantastic sensitivity on the part of living organisms, a sensitivity of which we have been hitherto completely unaware? Brown himself says: "The factors responsible for this may be quite subtle. One critical question in the problem is whether or not the organism possesses adequate sensitivity to perceive fluctuations in pervasive, subtle geophysical forces."[28] It has already been shown that these subtle forces are not among the obvious timegivers such as light, temperature, or pressure. What then is the identity of the mysterious factors whose existence Brown postulates?

A Bold Experiment

Physicists and astronomers have known for a long time that the earth's magnetic field varies according to the positions of the sun and the moon with respect to the earth. The magnetized end of the needle in a compass turns to the north, but when the effects of an eruption of sunspots reach the earth the needle will quiver on its pivot, recording these "magnetic storms." Thanks to the precise records kept in the observatories, the most minute changes can be noticed. In 1940, Chapman and Bartels discovered that the intensity and direction of magnetic fields undergo hourly modulations related to the lunar day and the lunar month.[29] Recently three British astronomers, Leaton, Malin, and Finch, have added precision to a successful confirmation of their discovery.[30]

Animals are able to follow the movement of solar and
lunar clocks without being exposed to them visually.
Adding the two findings together, Brown formulated the
following hypothesis: perhaps organisms respond to geophysical factors that follow from the relative position of
these two bodies, such as, for instance, terrestrial magnetism. If this were the case, the animal organism would be
some kind of a "living magnetometer," reacting in the
same way as the instrument of the geophysicists.

A first experiment conducted on various small animals
produced encouraging results. A correlation did emerge
between the metabolism of these animals, as measured
by oxygen consumption, and geomagnetic variations simultaneously registered by the observatories. These animals not only had a biological clock that regulated their
activity level in time, they also seemed to have a "biological compass needle," which permitted them to orient
themselves in space. And this biological compass needle
—like its metallic namesake—fluctuated according to
solar and lunar rhythms. But these first results needed
duplication. In order to verify the existence of such
sensitivity, Brown devised a series of ingenious experiments. From 1959 on, he studied, with his co-workers,
the behavior of animals placed in the geomagnetic field
according to well-defined orientations.[31]

The boldness of these experiments consists in the fact
that the geomagnetic field is *extremely weak*. Previous
researchers had failed to find any reaction from animals
even with the use of magnetic fields a hundred times as
strong as the natural fields that surround us. It appeared
obvious to them that Brown and his associates would obtain no results with their experimental conditions. To
expect them to find anything would have been tantamount to believing in the possibility that a beacon could

remain invisible because it was too bright, or that a horn could remain inaudible because it was too loud. But the analogy to light and sound is not always relevant; organisms sometimes respond more readily to weaker energy levels to be found in nature—and variations in terrestrial magnetism belong in this group. The excessive magnetic intensities used in previous experiments only caused a flooding of the animal, which resulted in its inability to react.[32]

The Biological Compass

Brown and his colleagues began their studies with a small mollusk called *Nassarius,* which resembles a slug and lives in puddles on the beach. These animals were chosen because of their slowness. The experimental setting, illustrated in Figure 4, was simple but original. The mollusks were placed inside a "corral" containing two centimeters of water. They could leave the container through the neck of the corral, but only one at a time. As they left the enclosure, a fan-shaped indicator permitted the experimenter to measure the angle of the direction taken by the animal in leaving its prison. In this fashion the exits of thirty-three thousand *Nassarius* were observed; some of the slugs turned left, some right, and some continued straight ahead. When the researchers submitted the pattern of exit orientation to mathematical analysis, they found that the direction in which the *Nassarius* turns upon leaving depends on the time of day. In the morning the mollusks usually turn right; at other times they turn left more often. Certain components of terrestrial magnetism also change in the course of the day. Continuing their experiments through the summer of 1959, Brown and his associates discovered that the mol-

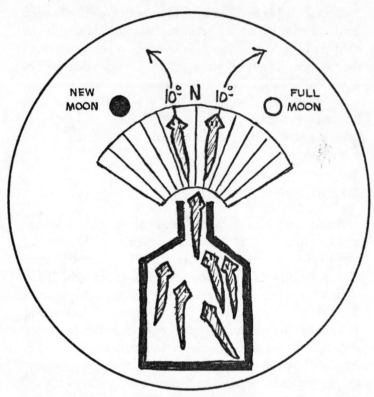

Fig. 4—*The Moon's Influence on the Biological Compass of Planaria (flatworm).*
Within the terrestrial magnetic field, the worms, upon leaving their enclosure, do not always turn in the same direction. Which way they turn depends on the phase of the moon. The indicator placed at the exit of their corral shows that at new moon they tend to turn left, about ten degrees from the north; at the full moon they tend to turn right. (After F. A. Brown, Jr., *Discovery*, November, 1963.)

lusks' rhythm of orientation is affected by the phase of the lunar month just as the sensitive registering needle of the geophysicist is.

A later experiment, conducted with small fresh-water worms called *Planaria,* produced similar results. The flatworm was influenced by the phases of the moon: at the new moon it turned on the average ten degrees left of the north, while at the full moon it turned the same distance to the right. Furthermore, while it was also possible to change the natural orientation of the earth's magnetic field artificially, the animals were able to find their orientation under severely changed conditions and could discriminate within fifteen degrees the orientation of a field.

It has been shown since in many laboratories that other organisms also show an extraordinary sensitivity to magnetism. J.D. Palmer of the University of Illinois observed it in animals less than a millimeter in size, called *Volvox*. Armed with great patience, he watched with a microscope as seven thousand *Volvox* left their enclosure through a diminutive exit, and concluded that their direction was not random but followed preferred orientations.[33] In Germany, G. Becker has shown that insects such as flies do not land in a chance direction but align themselves along certain lines of terrestrial magnetic force. The explanation given by Yeagley in 1947 for the return of pigeons in terms of magnetic lines[34] has lately been reformulated on a new basis; it now appears that pigeons are indeed equipped with extraordinary sensitivity to magnetism. Perhaps the whole problem of migrations, for such a long time impervious to any satisfactory explanation, will soon find a solution along these lines.

Electrical Perception

But magnetism is not the only additional sense that has been recently found to exist in animals; there are others that enable the organism to receive hitherto unknown messages from space. Animals are also sensible to the whole gamut of electromagnetic waves. For example, the behavior of a mouse was seen to change as a response to very weak gamma radiations, in a study that Brown conducted with Y.H. Park and J.R. Zeno.[35] Gamma radiations, which are very short electromagnetic waves, are carried to earth by cosmic rays originating from every corner of the universe; their weakness is due to the filtering by our atmosphere, which keeps these rays from reaching the earth's surface in damaging quantities.

The effect of electrostatic fields has also been studied. An electrostatic field develops all around a body that is electrically charged. "It was demonstrated," Brown writes,

> that animals such as snails and planarians are able to resolve differences in electrostatic fields of the order of strength of those to which they are steadily subjected in nature. The sensitivity which has been proven indicates the living thing to have more than 100 times the sensitivity which would be required, for instance, to "perceive" the electrical field created by a thundercloud rising miles away on the horizon.[36]

At the other end of the spectrum, H.L. König of Munich has been able to show, with the help of sensitive instruments, that the atmosphere contains waves of extremely low frequency (one to ten Hertz), but of great length—tens and hundreds of thousands of kilometers. On the surface these waves appear to be of a very low energy, yet they affect the sprouting of wheat, the growth of bacteria, and the activity of insects.[37] One of their characteristics is that nothing can stop them, not even the thickest walls. Another is that they depend on cosmic phenomena; both the rising of the sun and solar eruptions cause an abundance of such waves. Seeds, bacteria, and insects seem to "know" this and regulate their vital rhythms accordingly.

Gravitational Perception

Some scientists do not hesitate to claim that animals are also provided with a "gravitational eye." Gravitation enters everywhere; there is nothing on earth that can escape its effects. It also seems impervious to human manipulation; scientists encounter endless difficulty in trying to create artificial gravity in laboratories. There are instruments that record the slightest changes in gravitational forces. It is obvious that the mass of certain celestial bodies, such as the sun and the moon, greatly affects our earth. Were it not for the gravitational pull of the sun, the earth would be lost in the icy wastes of the cosmos. The moon in passing over the meridian of any given place causes tides, not only in the oceans, but also in the atmosphere and on the ground. All living things, no matter how small, react in each of their cells to the gravitational pull that follows from the movements of the sun and of the moon. While on a global scale these forces are considerable, their effect is infinitesimally small on the scale of living things.

Before Brown's discoveries, nobody would have dreamt of looking for biological effects tied to such tenuous influences. Recently, however, F. Schneider, a biologist in Zurich, began to investigate whether living organisms behave like ultra-sensitive gravimeters, setting their clocks by adapting to changes in gravity. His first success was in demonstrating that cockchafers, a kind of large beetle, respond to both magnetic and gravitational forces.[38] Confined in a container with opaque sides, a swarm of the insects reacted to the invisible approach of a mass of lead weighing eighty pounds or more. Such a reaction is still difficult to explain, but Schneider concluded:

In the absence of a more satisfactory explanation, one must admit that these insects are aware of modifications in the apportioning of masses in their immediate vicinity. Since in these experiments the gravitational fields of the sun and of the moon are stronger than that of the mass of lead, it seems likely that the movement of these celestial bodies must have a commensurate effect on behavior.[39]

According to Schneider, the insect may have an "ultra-optic" perception of gravitation that permits it to follow the movements of the sun and the moon and set its biological clock by them.

Subtle Rhythms

The apparently mysterious behavior of organisms isolated in laboratories begins to yield to some explanations. The question, are internal clocks closed systems that function independently of the environment, or are they open systems that can be advanced or retarded by forces originating outside, has been completely reformulated. Biological clocks do not function in a closed circuit; this, of course, does not exclude the fact that they do have an existence within the organisms themselves. It appears that these internal timing devices can be adjusted and reset by external forces: extremely small changes in atmospheric electricity, in the earth's magnetism, or in gravitational fields. In fact, all living things, whether animal or vegetable, when deprived of the "obvious rhythms" imposed by light, temperature, or pressure, seem to become extremely sensitive to the "subtle rhythms" of cosmic origin recently discovered. Scientists have begun to accept the idea, until recently unbelievable, that the influences of space penetrate everywhere, including the best protected laboratories, affecting all organisms, even those placed in apparently uniform conditions. In fact, the results show that there are no truly uniform conditions on earth.

Among humans, important changes in biological timing that also seem related to events in cosmic space have been observed for some time now. We will now turn our attention to the consequences of these phenomena on man himself.

NOTES TO CHAPTER EIGHT

1. J. Harker, "Diurnal Rhythms in the Animal Kingdom," *Biological Review*, XXXIII (1958), 1.
2. F.A. Brown, Jr., *Biological Clocks* (Boston: American Institute of Biological Sciences, 1962).
3. *Ibid.*
4. F. Halberg, "Physiologic Twenty-four-hour Rhythms: A Determinant of Response to Environmental Agents," in *Man's Dependence on the Earthly Atmosphere* (New York: Macmillan, 1962).
5. R.L. Carson, *The Sea Around Us* (Oxford University Press, 1950).
6. E. Bünning, *The Physiological Clock* (Berlin: Springer, 1964).
7. *Ibid.*
8. A. Reinberg and J. Ghata, *Rythmes et cycles biologiques* (Paris: P.U.F., 1957).
9. F.A. Brown, Jr., *op. cit.*
10. *Ibid.*
11. *Ibid.*
12. H.S. Burr, "Tree Potential and Sunspots," *Cycles*, October, 1964, 243.
13. N.S. Stcherbinovsky, "Cyclical Activity of the Sun and the Rhythm of Multiplication of Massive Organisms," in *The Earth in the Universe* (in Russian), (Moscow: 1964).
14. R. Hartland-Rowe, "The Biology of a Tropical Mayfly *Povilla Adusta Navas*, With Special Reference to the Lunar Rhythm of Emergence," *Rev. Zool. Botan. Africaine*, LVIII (1958), 185.
15. W.W. MacDonald, "Observations on the Biology of Chaoborids and Chironomids in Lake Victoria," *Journal of Animal Ecology*, XXV (1956), 36.
16. "Coraux fossiles et rotation de la Terre," *Atomes*, CCXXXIV (1966), 429.
17. *Ibid.*
18. F.A. Brown, Jr., "The Rhythmic Nature of Animals and Plants," *American Scientist*, XLVII (1959), No. 2, 164.

19. ——, *Biological Clocks, op. cit.*

20. ——, "Persistent Activity Rhythms in the Oyster," *American Journal of Physiology,* CLXXVIII (1954), 510.

21. F.A. Brown, Jr. and E. Terracini, "Exogenous Timing of Rat Spontaneous Activity Periods," *Proceedings of the Society of Experimental Biological Medicine,* CI (1959), No. 3, 457.

22. F.A. Brown, Jr., "Propensity for Lunar Periodicity in Hamsters," *Proceedings of the Society of Experimental Biological Medicine,* CXX (1965), 792.

23. L.G. Johnson, "Diurnal Patterns of Metabolic Variations in Chick Embryos," *Biological Bulletin,* CXXXI (1966), No. 2, 308.

24. F.A. Brown, Jr., *Biological Clocks, op. cit.*

25. *Ibid.*

26. F.A. Brown, Jr., "Living Clocks," *Science,* CXXX (1959), 1535.

27. L.C. Cole, "Biological Clock in the Unicorn," *Science,* CXXV (1957), 874.

28. F.A. Brown, Jr., *Biological Clocks, op. cit.*

29. J. Bartels and S. Chapman, *Geomagnetism* (Oxford University Press: 1940).

30. Leaton, Malin, and Finch, "The Solar and Luni-Solar Variation of the Geomagnetic Field at Greenwich and Abinger, 1916–1957," *Obs. Bull. G. B.,* LIII (1962), D 273–D 318.

31. F.A. Brown, Jr., "How Animals Respond to Magnetism," *Discovery,* November, 1963.

32. M. Gauquelin, "Effets biologiques des champs magnétiques," *Année Biologique,* V (1966), 595.

33. J.D. Palmer, "Organismic Spatial Orientation in Very Weak Magnetic Fields," *Nature,* CXCVIII (1963), 1061.

34. H.L. Yeagley, "A Preliminary Study of a Physical Basis of Bird Navigation," *Journal of Applied Physics,* XVIII (1947), 1035.

35. F.A. Brown, Y. Park and J. Zeno, "Diurnal Variation in Organismic Response to Very Weak Gamma Radiation," *Nature,* CCXI (1966), 830.

36. F.A. Brown, Jr., *Biological Clocks, op. cit.*

37. H. König and F. Ankermüller, "Ueber den Einfluss besonders niederfrquenter elektrischer Vorgänge in der Atmosphäre auf den Menschen," *Naturwissenschaft,* XXI (1960), 483.

38. F. Schneider, "Die Beeinflussung der Ultraoptischen Orientierung der Maikäfer durch Veränderung des lokalen Massenverteilungsmusters," *Revue Suisse de Zoologie,* LXXI (1964), 632.

39. *Ibid.*

The Unknown Senses of Man

Scientists began the study of the effects of cosmic phenomena on man with hesitation because they were running the danger of becoming identified with outdated superstitious beliefs. But the progress of science made it inevitable that the question be framed again; there was no other alternative, since it is obvious that the human organism too is ruled by external rhythms as well as internal ones. There are seasonal and daily rhythms, of course, but there are also more mysterious ones. The new history of the influences of the cosmos on man began shortly after World War II.

The Adventure of Drs. Faure and Sardou

In 1920 there lived in the south of France a physician, Dr. Faure, who one day made a deeply perplexing observation. In his own words:

> "I was in Nice, a town where automatic telephones had been installed . . . on certain days the sets would not work or worked erratically for a few hours, yet there was nothing inside the mechanism that could explain the malfunction. Then all of a sudden the line would be clear again, without any human intervention. It

rather surprised me to learn that these temporary troubles with the telephone were accompanied by an increased incidence of illnesses, and preceded severe atmospheric perturbations. On one of the days that the telephone had been on the blink for quite a long time, I read in the news that a strong magnetic storm in the United States had disrupted telephone and telegraphic communications for several hours. When I asked M. Vallot (an astronomer) about it, he related that such perturbations were not at all rare, and that they also affected the stability of compasses, the appearance of northern lights, seismic tremors, volcanic eruptions, and so forth. According to him, one of the most probable causes of these magnetic disturbances was the passage of a major sunspot across the meridian. So we resolved to research together whether the passage of sunspots did also coincide with the recrudescence of human sickness.

Doctor Sardou, who became acquainted with our project, offered his collaboration, and we embarked on our first research. M. Vallot, in his laboratory on Mount Blanc, recorded the passage of sunspots. At the same time Dr. Sardou recorded the cases of sickness he observed at Nice on the Mediterranean shore, while I recorded those at Lamalou, a station in the Cevennes hills on the borders of the central plateau of France. Our observations were not relayed to each other. But when we matched our results after 267 days of continuous observations, it was easy to see that they were in a chronological sequence; that is, the 25 transitions of sunspots were followed 21 times by a clear incidence of morbidity. . . . Later I also noticed that the number of sudden deaths during the passage of sunspots was twice as high as at any other time."[1]

The findings of Faure, Sardou, and Vallot were communicated to the Academy of Medicine of Paris on July 4,

1922. That date marks the beginnings of the modern history of cosmic influences on man.

Tchijevsky's History

At the same time, A.L. Tchijevsky, a professor of history living in Moscow, was poring over the ancient chronicles of his country. He was puzzled by the apparent rhythms revealed in the cyclical events of humanity: the social movements of history, epidemics, etc. One day he thought of relating the periodic activity of sunspots with the different phenomena that up to that time had not been explained by a known law. After many years of work, Tchijevsky assembled a thorough record of recurring social events and compared it with the fluctuation in the number of sunspots. The study he produced was a truly panoramic view of history, in which he correlated the curves of solar activity with wars, revolutions, and migrations, all the way from 500 B.C. to the year 1900. Tchijevsky concluded the analysis of his results by noting that psychic epidemics coincided with solar activity peaks 72 per cent of the time and with troughs in solar activity only 28 per cent of the time.[2]

For Tchijevsky, even the immigration of Jews into the United States followed a cosmic determinism, just as the alternation of Liberal and Conservative cabinets in England did. In the century between 1830 and 1930, the Liberals are supposed to have been in power during sunspot peaks and the Conservatives when sunspots were scarce. According to Tchijevsky, solar activity facilitates unrest, and it is this unrest that caused the Jews to try a new life across the sea and encouraged the English electorate to support less traditional candidates.

But Tchijevsky did not stop there. He also collected information about the great epidemics that had devastated Russia and the rest of the world. His results were quite impressive; the great plagues, the fatal diphtheria and cholera scourges of Europe, the Russian typhus, and the smallpox epidemics of Chicago all seemed to follow the sun's eleven-year periodicity. The investigator claimed that it was the peaks of solar activity that seemed to affect terrestrial life adversely. Epidemics tended to occur during years of maximum activity and abated in years when the sun was quiet[3] (*see* Fig. 5).

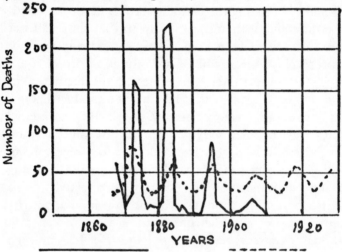

Frequency of deaths due to Smallpox • Number of Sunspots (R.)

Fig. 5—*Smallpox Epidemics in Chicago and Sunspots*
According to Tchijevsky, the maximum number of deaths from smallpox before the vaccine was introduced coincided with peaks in solar activity through several consecutive cycles. (After Berg, *Symposium Internationale sur les Relations Phénomenales Solaires et Terrestriale* [Brussels: Presses Académiques Européennes, 1960], p. 164.)

The publication of this work in the U.S.S.R. caused Tchijevsky great difficulty. In the period between the two world wars Russia was under the rigid rule of Stalin, and the claim that sunspots could influence man's life was considered a denial of some of the doctrines of dialectical materialism. As a result, Tchijevsky was sent away to Siberia to meditate on the dangers of leaving the well-traveled paths of science in order to open up new directions. When Khrushchev came to power, however, Tchijevsky was completely rehabilitated and allowed to take up his researches again.[4] Unfortunately, he died shortly afterward, on December 20, 1964.

Sometimes the history of science runs parallel to history with a capital "H." It has to be admitted that Tchijevsky's observations—like Faure's—sometimes lacked strictness and that his systematic conclusions included a certain amount of exaggeration. Because of this, many scientists have for a long time refused to believe that cosmic influences could have any impact on human life and behavior. Yet we owe Tchijevsky and Faure a great debt for having posed the old question in new terms. There is no doubt that they sighted a new continent—but the real adventure was yet to begin.

Takata's History

Maki Takata, a physician and professor at Toho University in Tokyo, was born in Japan in 1892. Shortly before World War II he encountered the problem that was to lead to his discovery of a mysterious relationship between, of all things, human blood and the sun. By that time he was well known for having developed a test, called the "Takata reaction," which involves the chemical testing of albumin in blood serum. Albumin is an organic colloid; Takata's reaction gives an index for its floculation—its propensity for curdling into small tufty lumps. It is a delicate method to carry through: first, the blood is taken and processed; then a reagent that stimulates floculation is added to it. If little reagent is needed for floculation to begin, it is said that the floculation index is high; when much reagent is needed, the index is low. In males this index was supposedly constant, while in females it varied depending on the menstrual cycle. This made Takata's reaction a basic analytical tool for gynecologists.

In January, 1938, however, every hospital that used Takata's reaction reported that the index of floculation had suddenly begun to rise for males and females alike. The change affected at the same time subjects far removed from each other across the globe. Takata began some experiments in Tokyo, to be paralleled by his co-worker Murasugi at Kobe, a town in the far south of Japan. Each day for four months in 1939 they measured the floculation index of two experimental subjects. When these indices were later compared, Takata noticed that the two curves of daily variation were perfectly parallel. During the whole four-month period, for each peak on one of the curves there was a corresponding sudden rise on the other graph—when the serum of the man in Tokyo was "high," so was that of the man in Kobe, about a hundred miles away. Takata concluded that the phenomenon must have been worldwide and due to cosmic factors.[5]

For twenty years the Japanese biologist continued collecting observations, establishing the existence of strange ties between the floculation of blood serum and several cosmic events. His experiments show, in fact, that the changes in the serum occur in particular when a group of sunspots passes across the central meridian of the sun, that is, when the sun directs a concentrated beam of waves and particles toward the earth.

Takata also noted an interesting effect of the sun that had previously gone unnoticed: the floculation index, very low during the end of the night, showed a sudden rise at the coming of day. The amazing fact is that the increase of the curve begins a few minutes *before* sunrise, as if the blood somehow "foresees" the appearance of the sun (*see* Fig. 6). Our preceding chapter may have accus-

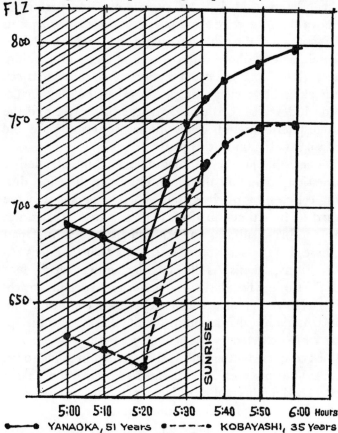

Fig. 6—*Blood Serum and the Sunrise*
The floculation index of blood serum (FLZ) shows a sudden increase a few minutes before sunrise. The graph reports the floculation indices of two subjects tested on September 4, 1940, at Kobe, Japan. (After M. Takata, *Symposium Internationale sur les Relations Phénomenales Solaire et Terrestriale* [Brussels: Presses Académiques Européennes, 1960], p. 172.)

tomed us to such incredible "foresight" on the part of living things, but Takata was at the time unaware of the various experimental results that would have helped to explain his finding. To assure himself that the effects he observed were due to solar radiation, he decided to see what happened when an experiment was performed above the protective atmospheric screen that isolates us from much of the sun's activity. In an airplane he flew to an altitude of above thirty thousand feet with a volunteer whose blood was taken every fifteen minutes to check the effect of varying altitude. As predicted, the floculation index rose spectacularly as the plane rose and the atmospheric shield became thinner, confirming the role of solar radiation in this matter.

Then the Japanese biologist asked himself another question: Wouldn't the moon eliminate the effect during eclipses, by placing itself between the sun and the earth? Three times, in 1941, 1943, and 1948, Takata was able to bring subjects and equipment to areas in Japan where there was a total eclipse—and each time he verified his hypothesis. As the moon began to cover the face of the sun the floculation index started to decline, reaching its lowest point when the eclipse was complete. The solar radiation that accounts for the Takata effect is apparently deflected by the moon; yet neither houses nor thick concrete battlements had succeeded in doing so before. The only previous experiment in which the Takata effect had not been observed took place in a mine shaft at Mieken, six hundred feet underground.

A tremendously strong solar radiation is involved here, one that is almost impossible to stop. This immediately reminds us of Brown's observation that spatial influences penetrate the most carefully sheltered experimental conditions. Some elements of the human body, sheltered as they are within the blood vessels, are still exposed to the vagaries of that great cosmic clock, the sun. It was Takata himself who formulated the concise definition: "Man is a living sun-dial."[6] The sudden increase in the indices of floculation in the year 1938 was finally explained as following a marked increase in solar activity after several years of quiet. The task of discovering the nature of these piercing rays is still undone; Takata has attempted it, but without success. Neither he nor his followers have yet discovered exactly how the influence works. This is partly due to the fact that cosmic agents are unpredictable—they cannot be tamely manipulated as other laboratory agents are. But the Takata effect has given us the key to a biological mystery.

The Story of Nicolas Schulz

The recent work of the Soviet hematologist Nicolas Schulz has clarified the relationship of certain properties of human blood to cosmic phenomena. With Schulz's work we leave the uncertain history of pioneering efforts and enter the well-charted era of perfectly verified scientific research. The results of his work from 1954 on were published by Schulz in the 1960 reports of the U.S.S.R. Academy of Sciences. They were based on more than 120,000 measurements taken at Sotchi, a resort on the shores of the Black Sea. Schulz concluded that the vagaries of the solar clock modify the lymphocytic ratio of the blood considerably.[7] In the years 1957–58, physicians had noticed an abnormal increase of some components of blood, lymphocytes in particular. The causes of this phenomenon remained unknown. Some thought it was due to the aftereffects of war-time deprivation, malnutrition, or fatigue. But these explanations did not always hold—only solar activity accounted consistently for the facts. In 1957 the number of sunspots reached a peak. Under the direction of Dr. Schulz, the Soviet researchers did bloodcounts on thousands of healthy subjects and compared their results with the intensity of the sun's activity. An almost perfect parallel was found between the percentage of lymphocytes and the sunspot frequencies posted each month by the astronomical observatories.[8]

Sometimes a disease results from a deficit of certain blood components. During the great solar explosions of February, 1956, blood analyses conducted throughout the Soviet Union showed a marked rise in leukopenia, or abnormal decrease in certain white blood cells. Before the solar eruption, the percentage of leukopenics—those with less than five thousand leukocytes per cubic mm. of blood—was 14 per cent of the population. After the eruption the percentage doubled to 29 per cent; one month later, in March, it was back to 13 per cent; by July it was 12 per cent; and by October it was 11 per cent. Solar activity was therefore able to explain something previously inexplicable: the constant change in the blood-component ratio in people of good health. It was known, of course, that such variations depend also on terrestrial factors such as age, exertion, and nutrition, but never before had it been thought that the differences might have cosmic origins.

Dr. De Rudder's Question

How did weak individuals, those whose diseased organisms offered scant resistance to external threats, react to such changes in the blood? The first to formulate this question clearly was Professor B. De Rudder of the Uni-

versity of Frankfurt-am-Main, in his work *Grundriss
einer Meteorobiologie des Menschen (An Outline of
Human Meteorobiology).*[9] There are certain sudden ill-
esses, such as infarction of the myocardium, angina
pectoris, or pulmonary embolism, that are called "mete-
orotropic" because of their seeming dependence on atmospheric conditions. People who suffer from certain
diseases are particularly sensitive to changes in the
weather. Sometimes amputees inexplicably feel pain in
their missing limbs; rheumatics and arthritics were fore-
casting changes in the weather long before meteorological instruments were developed. It has also been known
that some people are able to tell weather conditions from
their sickbeds—while no less isolated from the outside
than Brown's sealed oysters. No explanation of these diverse phenomena had been forthcoming until De Rudder
raised the possibility that they were due to cosmic factors, and in the last twenty years observations from all
around the world have been confirming his hunch: atmospheric conditions and human physiology are very
closely linked.

Infarction of the Myocardium

Professor Romensky, Director of the Board of Health
at Sotchi on the Black Sea, reported that on May 18, 1959,
the number of cardiovascular incidents suddenly rose to
twenty in the hospitals under his jurisdiction; the previous daily quota had only been two. On May 17 of that
year an exceptional solar event took place: the observatory of the U.S.S.R. Academy of Sciences noted the onset
of three powerful solar explosions traveling toward the
earth at a speed of about ten thousand miles per second.
Particles from the solar explosion reached the earth the

next day, May 18. The cause-and-effect relationship seems obvious, especially since Dr. Romensky had already, in 1956, reported similar coincidences: the number of cardiovascular patients in Sotchi had increased threefold from February to August, a period of energetic solar activity.[10]

At the International Geophysical and Meteorological Convention of 1960, in Ottawa, Dr. Giordano reported the results of a statistical analysis on the number of infarctions of the myocardium observed in Pavia, Italy, from 1954 to 1958. Between these two dates, solar activity was increasing. The incidence of infarctions was also on the increase: from a yearly total of 200 cases in 1954, it climbed to 450 in 1958.[11] A careful case-by-case analysis allowed Dr. Giordano to conclude that certain days are "infarction days," while others are free of the incidence of this disease. The French physician Poumailloux, working with Viart, a meteorologist, developed this line of research even further. In a communication to the Academy of Medicine in Paris, they showed that infarctions do not occur by chance, but follow well-defined solar coordinates.[12] These two specialists reported that for the year 1957 there was a very high correlation between the number of infarctions and sudden increases in solar activity. When a disturbance was produced on the solar surface, this appeared a little later to affect the blood vessels, causing the formation of clots in individuals so predisposed. The bloodclots then obstructed the coronary artery, precipitating a fatal infarction.

Tuberculosis

Two German researchers, G. and B. Düll, had in 1934 reported some important statistics on deaths by tuberculosis in Hamburg, Copenhagen, and Zurich, in connection with the dates of violent solar explosions. On days of peak activity, the number of deaths was much higher than either before or after.[13] A few years later Dr. Lingemann did a study in Western Germany relating solar activity to the incidence of pulmonary hemorrhage. Through the four years of his study, from 1948 to 1952, Dr. Lingemann kept in close touch with the astronomical observatories of his country. He found, to his own surprise, that the most dangerous days for his patients tended to be the ones on which Northern Lights were seen over Germany. And, of course, Northern Lights are caused by a strong solar activity disturbing the upper layers of the atmosphere.[14] In the southern hemisphere Dr. Puig noted a threefold increase in respiratory ailments on days of strong solar activity.[15] There has been, however, one exception: Dr. H. Berg of Cologne failed to find, in a 1953 study, any relationship between frequency of pulmonary embolism and cosmic causes.[16] But otherwise all studies agree that sunspot activity spells danger for those with pulmonary disease.

There are many other observations being collected, for example, those about eclampsia, a serious attack of convulsions that occurs during pregnancy. Gynecologists and midwives long ago noticed that eclampsia goes in waves, and, as a result, they blamed changes in the weather for it. In 1942, two German doctors, Bach and Schluck, began to investigate the question scientifically.[17] They found that the illness did in fact follow a cyclical pattern, but that weather change was not one of its causes. The sun's activity, however, played a major role: days on which the sun had been quiet yielded few cases of eclampsia, but the waves of the sickness mounted on days when the sun had been active.

Effects on the Nervous System

Ten years ago, Dr. Martini compared the frequency of coal mining incidents in the Ruhr with solar activity.[18] Catastrophes due to natural causes, such as the formation of gases, or to failure of material, such as the breaking of scaffolds, were not included; he counted only accidents caused by the human element. His data are based on 306 working days, which accounted for 5,580 accidents. Dr. Martini feels that the results leave no room for doubt: the miners had significantly more accidents on days following solar eruptions; days on which the sun was quiet were followed by a decrease in the number of accidents. Another scientist, Dr. Reiter, has compiled some data on the number of traffic accidents in Bavaria during 1952.[19] By mapping the date and the hour of 130,-000 such accidents, he found a 10 per cent increase in their occurrence on days following solar eruptions. Both authors believe that solar explosions disturb the reflexes of the miner and the driver by, respectively, affecting terrestrial magnetism and increasing the quantity of the long atmospheric waves. It appears that reactions measured in the laboratory are also slower on days of magnetic storms.

The Dülls have also produced a study in which they recorded the daily frequencies of suicides and acute mental disorders during a four-year period.[20] By comparing this frequency curve with the chronology of sixty-seven magnetic storms recorded during the same interval, the authors determined what they thought was a very clear correlation: while the magnetic storms lasted, the number of suicides and mental disturbances increased considerably. To a specialist such as Dr. Berg, however, the statistics employed in this research were lacking in strictness.

Recently the work of the two Germans has been taken up again, with more satisfactory methods, by a team of three New York scientists, Howard Friedman, Robert O. Becker, and Charles H. Bachman. They recorded the number of daily admissions in eight large psychiatric hospitals in New York and compared it with variations in the daily magnetic index developed at the Magnetic Observatory in Fredericksburg, Virginia. The index reflects, hour by hour, the magnetic activity of the sun. During the period under study, from July 1, 1957, to October 30, 1961, there were 28,642 admissions reported in the hospitals sampled. The statistical analysis clearly shows that admissions increase on days of strong magnetic disturbance. The authors conclude their study as follows:

> The results are in keeping with the conception of the behavior of an organism being significantly influenced through the direct current control system, by external force fields. Attention is thus invited to a hitherto neglected dimension in the complexity of psychopathology specifically, and perhaps generally in all human behavior.[21]

How can man—or the animals that Brown has studied—be affected by terrestrial magnetism? In a later article, Dr. Becker makes the following postulate: "Subtle changes in the intensity of the geomagnetic field may affect the nervous system by altering the body's own electromagnetic field."[22]

"Lunacy"

From the most ancient times, the moon has been charged with a disturbing influence on mental stability.

"Lunatic" has become a synonym for "unruly spirit" or "madman." "As early as the sixteenth century," writes Dr. Ravitz,

> Paracelsus claimed that the insane grew worse at the dark of the moon when the moon's attraction upon the brain was believed to be the strongest. Such beliefs were legalized in eighteenth century England, at which time a distinction was made between "insane," which designated the chronically and hopelessly psychotic, and "lunatic" aberrations which were believed to be exacerbated only by the full moon. Prior to 1808, Bethlehem hospital inmates were beaten at certain lunar periods as a prophylaxis against violence.[23]

The Philadelphia Police Department is still of the opinion that certain criminal acts coincide with the phases of the moon. At the end of 1961, it published a report for the American Institute of Medical Climatology entitled "Effect of Full Moon on Human Behavior." Inspector Wilfred Faust stated:

> The seventy-odd policemen who deal with telephone complaints have always reported that activity—especially crimes against persons—seemed to increase as the night of the full moon drew near. People whose antisocial behavior had psychotic roots—such as firebugs, kleptomaniacs, destructive drivers, and homicidal alcoholics—seemed to go on a rampage as the moon rounded, calming down as the moon waned.[24]

Yet most psychologists and sociologists are not ready to believe in the influence of the moon on criminal impulses. Although they recognize that mental illnesses are often cyclical, they also note that not all biological rhythms are tied to cosmic cycles, just as not every cosmic cycle has to have an effect on human rhythms. Scientists have also denied the effect of the moon because their instruments could not find a trace of it. A similar situation prevailed in the sixteenth century, when Galileo himself wrote on the subject of the moon's influence on the tides that it "did not exist at all, except as superstition"! In his time, there was no tangible proof of a relationship between the moon and the tides except for sailors' and fishermen's tales. Besides, the relationship is far from perfect, since irregular coastlines sometimes slow down the flow of the tides long after the culmination of the moon. It was not until Newton formulated the laws of universal gravitation that the moon's influence on the oceans was finally accepted.

Today scientists are again beginning to change their opinions, as their more sensitive instruments start to show lunar influences. A short time ago it was found that the phases of the moon bring about modulations in the earth's electric and magnetic fields. Such measurable modulations may affect mental disorders. Dr. Leonard J. Ravitz, neurological and psychiatric consultant at the Virginia Department of Health and Education, has been measuring for some years the differences in electric potential between the head and the chest of mental patients. Such differences were found to change from day to day; they followed a cyclical pattern even in normal subjects. According to Dr. Ravitz, the cycles paralleled seasonal and lunar changes. "In the fall and winter maximal positivity tends to occur around new moon and maximal negativity around full moon," he wrote.[25] The effects of the moon seem to be more pronounced on mental patients than on normal persons since the difference in potential is markedly greater for the former. Dr. Ravitz cites the example of a twenty-seven-year-old schizophrenic whose symptoms grew worse at the new moon and the full moon, just when the differences in electric potential between his head and chest were greatest. This pattern did not suggest to Ravitz that the moon affects human behavior directly, but that by modifying the ratio of terrestrial electromagnetic forces the moon could precipitate disorders in persons whose mental balance is precarious.

Biology and the Moon

In 1940 Dr. William Petersen of Chicago noted that deaths caused by tuberculosis were most frequent seven days before the full moon, and sometimes eleven days before. He related this pattern to the lunar cycle of terrestrial magnetism, which, according to him, varies with the pH content of the blood, that is, its ratio of acidity to alkalinity.[26] More recently, a German physician, Heckert, claimed significant correlations between the lunar phases and a variety of biological phenomena, such as the number of deaths, the occurrence of cases of pneumonia, and the amount of uric acid in the blood.[27]

While we are waiting for the verdict of the statisticians to be passed on the value of the above observations, every day there are new reports on the alleged biological effects of the moon. Darrell Huff, for instance, reports the following observation:

> A Florida surgeon, an ear-nose-throat man, has found remarkably clear evidence of a moon cycle in bleeding. Reporting in the *Journal* of the Florida Medical Association, Dr. Edson J. Andrews, of Tallahassee, tells what he found when he plotted cases of excessive post-operative bleeding against the cycles of the moon. Working with more than a thousand cases, and defining "bleeders" as patients requiring unusual means of hemostasis

on the operating table or requiring return to the operating room because of hemorrhaging, he found a sharp
difference. It amounted to a great preponderance of
bleeders near the time of the full moon and only an
insignificant number at the new moon. In the interval
between the first quarter and one day before the third
quarter, 82 per cent of all the cases occurred.[28]

Dr. Andrews admits that he knows of no scientific explanation for these facts. Yet he does not hesitate to add,
"These data have been so conclusive and convincing to
me, I threaten to become a witch doctor and operate on
dark nights only, saving the moonlit nights for romance."
It would be interesting to know whether other doctors
have had experiences similar to those of Dr. Andrews.

The Menstrual Cycle

The marked similarity between the average length of
a woman's menstrual cycle and the period between two
new moons has always puzzled man's imagination. Is this
just a chance coincidence, or is there a cause and effect
relationship involved?

In 1898 Svante Arrhenius, a Swede, reported on the
onset of 11,807 menstrual periods. He concluded that
their frequency during the waxing moon was higher than
during the waning moon, reaching a peak on the new
moon's eve.[29] Dr. Kirchhoff of Frankfurt confirmed these
results in 1935. A year later two other German doctors,
Gutman and Oswald, again found a peak at new moon,
but they also found one at the full moon. It should be
added that there have been physicians who have failed to
find any lunar influence on the beginning of menstruation. The research of the gynecologist Gunn, conducted
in 1938, is considered a classic work of careful precision.

In order to collect his data in a perfectly objective fashion, he asked his subjects to mail a signed postcard on the day menstruation started. The date of cancellation on the postcard was used as the datum of the study; Gunn waited until he had collected ten thousand cards. His work bore no fruits: in his sample there was no relationship between the lunar cycle and the day of onset of menstruation.[30] In 1951 the head of the Martinsklinik of Göttingen, Dr. Hosemann, reviewed all the existing literature on this question and concluded that the balance was negative, suggesting a skeptical attitude toward the existence of any relationship. Yet he himself, with Bauman as his co-worker, showed that there was a slight increase in the frequency of onset during the new moon in a sample of ten thousand cases.[31]

At this point, without facing the basic issues involved, the consensus of the majority of published reports suggests that there is a lunar cycle that seems more favorable to the onset of the menstrual cycle: that of the full moon. How can this statement be reconciled with the fact that the female menstrual cycle is not always of the same length as the lunar cycle—that it can, in fact, be several days shorter or longer? In commenting on this objection, Brown writes:

> This has led many scientists to the conclusion that such a rhythm can have no dependence whatsoever on the moon, and to ridicule popular notions to the contrary. A good, objective scientist never ridicules a belief; he simply asks whether the belief rests upon adequate evidence. It is quite possible that even these approximately monthly rhythms depend upon the moon.[32]

The problem certainly needs to be examined in greater detail. It is not at all unreasonable to assume that there are some privileged portions in the lunar cycle when, because of electromagnetic or other similar changes, the onset of menstruation would be facilitated. Perhaps the full moon is one such period. At least this hypothesis would be in accordance with Brown's findings on the use of the lunar clock by animal species.

The Unknown Senses of Man

Thus it seems that man, as well as animals, should have some extra senses for receiving the messages of the universe. By what means do such messages reach the human organism? The cosmic effects measured by our instruments are so weak that it is highly unlikely that they would have any effect on the human body. Yet we have to recognize that the "subtle synchronizers" do affect man. About forty years ago, for example, the Russian Tchijevsky demonstrated how human behavior and metabolism were affected by ions, electrically charged particles floating in the atmosphere. This was proof of a very fine sensitivity on the part of the human system. Recent investigations by Krueger and Smith,[33] and by Kornblueh and his collaborators,[34] have shown that the body can distinguish positive from negative ions: the former have a generally depressing effect, the latter a stimulating one. Physicists have shown that cosmic events affect atmospheric ionization—thus their influence on man can be explained through the medium of ionization.

An even more recent discovery is that of two German scientists, König and Reiter.[35] They found that the human organism is incredibly sensitive to waves of extremely low frequencies and correspondingly weak energy. It was theoretically unthinkable that man could register energy changes of such infinitesimal magnitude, but König and Reiter were not deterred by theoretical opinion. When they studied the reaction time of fifty-three thousand subjects and compared the results with the pattern of extremely long waves, they found that reaction time is considerably slowed down by such waves. Their results could explain the increase in the frequency of accidents at the time of solar eruptions reported by Reiter and Martini, on which we commented above. It is in the hours following the great solar perturbations that the behavior of extremely low frequency waves becomes very abnormal. According to H. Burr of Yale, the human brain and the central nervous system in general are the most elaborate stations for the reception of electromagnetic waves known in nature. König has remarked that the pattern of very low frequency waves is almost indistinguishable from the electroencephalogram wave pattern instruments record from the human brain.[36] As the brain is the center for the control of reactions, the relationship is plausible.

Magnetic Man

Further evidence of extraordinary human sensitivity to small magnetic changes was reported in 1962 by Y. Rocard, Professor of Physics at the Sorbonne.[37] Rocard was puzzled by the ancient claims of the dowsers, persons who pretend to be able to detect the presence of underground water. The dowser "knows" he has found water when the tip of a forked branch points downward by itself. Despite the superstitions involved, Rocard decided to study these claims scientifically. He succeeded in discovering very weak changes in terrestrial magnetism caused by the presence of water in the soil, which could produce a relaxation in the dowser's muscles, making his stick dip. Rocard conducted several experiments on sub-jects who were not professional dowsers. He found that the capacity for detecting weak magnetic gradients is not rare at all. An average subject discriminates between magnetic changes from .3 to .5 m0e/m, which would seem much too small to be detected except that they are of the same order of magnitude found among animals by biologists.

Rocard's results did not confirm all the dowsers' claims; on the contrary, he succeeded in delimiting the range of their actual accomplishments. He found that one cannot tell the presence of either still underground water or water running underground; only filtering water or water in contact with clay deposits will cause changes in magnetic gradient on the ground. Moreover, magnetic changes can be due to different sources; thus the dowser can be misled into thinking he has found water when in fact his stick has dipped because of buried metallic ob-jects, which produce similar effects. The "dowser's sign" can be induced by underground iron ore deposits, rocks hit by lightning, or even by nearby railroad cars, auto-mobiles, or other masses of metal on the surface.

Rocard's findings should certainly discourage anyone who wants to hire a dowser to find a place for boring a well in his field; on the other hand, they prove that man possesses an extremely fine sensitivity to fluctuations in terrestrial magnetism. Although Rocard's discoveries do not deal directly with cosmic clocks, they are relevant to our main concern. Magnetic irregularities are not only caused by what is found underground; the sun and the moon also modulate the terrestrial magnetic field. Changes registered following solar storms and lunar tran-sitions are of the same order of magnitude as those per-

ceived by Rocard's subjects: his findings confirm the fact
that man's magnetic sense enables him to "read" the solar
and lunar clocks.

It is now easier to understand why so many researchers
have found that human behavior and sanity are affected
by magnetic storms. Thanks to these additional senses,
man is enabled to establish a running dialogue with the
cosmos. The dialogue takes place through electrical channels and through other channels of whose existence we
are as yet unaware. They are the interpreters that trans-
late into biological language the majestic directives sent
to us through space by the cosmic clocks.

NOTES TO CHAPTER NINE

1. R. Tocquet, *Cycles et rythmes* (Paris: Dunod, 1951).
2. A.L. Tchijevsky, "L'action de l'activité périodique solaire sur les phénomènes sociaux," *Traité de Climatologie biologique et médicale* (Paris: Masson, 1934).
3. ———, "L'action de l'activité périodique solaire sur les épidémies," *op. cit.*
4. ———, *Le soleil et nous* (in Russian) (Moscow: 1963).
5. M. Takata and T. Murasugi, "Flockungszahlstörungen im gesunden menschlichen Serum, 'kosmoterrestrischer Sympathismus,'" *Bioklimat. Beibl.*, VIII (1941), 17.
6. M. Takata, "Ueber eine neue biologisch wirksame Komponente der Sonnenstrahlung, *Archiv Met. Geophys. Bioklimat.*, (1951), p. 486.
7. N. Schulz, "Lymphocytoses relatives et activité solaire," *Revue Médicale de Nancy*, June, 1961.
8. ———, "Les globules blancs des sujets bien portants et les taches solaires," *Toulouse Medical*, X (1960), 741.
9. B. de Rudder, *Grundriss einer Meteobiologie des Menschen* (Berlin: Springer, 1952).
10. N.V. Romensky, *Recueil des travaux scientifiques de l'administration des stations thermales et climatériques* (Sotchi, 1960).
11. A. Giordano, *Geofisica e Meteorologia*, VIII (1960), No. 3-4, 3.
12. J. Poumailloux and R. Viart, "Corrélations possibles entre l'incidence des infarctus du myocarde et l'augmentation des activités solaire et geomagnetique," *Bull. Acad. Med.*, CXLIII (1959), No. 7-8, 167.
13. T. and B. Düll, "Ueber die Abhängigkeit des Gesundheitszustandes von plötzlichen Eruptionen auf der Sonne und die Existenz einer 27-tägigen Periode in den Sterbefällen," *Virschow Archiv*, CXCII (1934), 972.
14. O. Lingemann, "Tuberkulöses Lungenbluten und meteorobiologische Einflüsse," *Der Tuberkulosarzt*, IX (1955), 261.
15. I. Puig, "El sol e la tuberculosis," *Publicaciones del Observ. de San Miguel, Buenos Aires*, No. 1 (1935).

16. H. Berg, *Solar-terrestrische Beziehungen in Meteorologie und Biologie* (Leipzig: Geest u. Portig, 1957).
17. E. Bach and L. Schluck, "Untersuchungen über den Einfluss von meteorologischen, ionosphärischen und solaren Faktoren, sowie den Mondphasen auf die Auslösung von Eklampsie und Präeklampsie," *Zentr. Blatt f. Gynäkol.*, LXVI (1942), 196.
18. R. Martini, "Der Einfluss der Sonnentätigkeit auf die Häufung von Unfällen," *Zentr. Bl. Arbeitsmedizin,* II (1952), 98.
19. R. Reiter, "Beziehungen zwischen Sommeneruptionen, Wetterablauf und Reaktionen des Menschen," *Z. Angew. Met.,* 1 (1953), 289.
20. T. and B. Düll, *op. cit.*
21. H. Friedman, R. Becker, and C. Bachman, "Geomagnetic Parameters and Psychiatric Hospital Admissions," *Nature,* CC (1963), 626.
22. "Magnetic Man," *Newsweek,* May 13, 1963.
23. D. Huff, *Cycles in Your Life* (London: V. Gollancz, 1965).
24. *Ibid.*
25. L. Ravitz, "Periodic Changes in Electromagnetic Fields," *Annals of the New York Academy of Science,* LCVIII (1960), 1181.
26. W. Petersen, *Man, Weather, Sun* (Springfield, Ill.: Charles Thomas, 1947).
27. H. Heckert, *Lunationsrythmen des menschlichen Organismus* (Leipzig: Geest u. Portig, 1961).
28. Huff, *op. cit.*
29. S. Arrhenius, "Die Einwirkung kosmischer Einflüsse auf physiologische Verhältinisse," *Skand. Arch. Physiol.,* VIII (1898), 367.
30. D. Gunn, P. Jenkin, and A. Gunn, "Menstrual Periodicity: Statistical Observations on a Large Sample of Normal Cases," *Journal of Obstetrical Gynaecology,* XLIV (1937), 839.
31. H. Hosemann, "Bestehen solare und lunare Einflüsse auf die Nativität und den Menstruationszyklus?" *Z. f. Geburtshilfe u. Gynäkol.,* CXXXIII (1950), No. 3, 263.
32. F.A. Brown, Jr., *Biological Clocks* (Boston: American Institute of Biological Sciences, 1962).
33. A. Krueger and R. Smith, "The Physiological Significance of Positive and Negative Ionization of the Atmosphere," in *Man's*

Dependence on the Earthly Atmosphere (New York: Macmillan, 1962).

34. I. Kornblueh, G. Piersol, and F. Speicher, *American Journal of Physiological Medicine*, XXXVII (1958), 18.

35. H. König and F. Ankermüller, "Ueber den Einfluss besonders niederfrquenter elektrischer Vorgänge in der Atmosphäre auf den Menschen," *Naturwissenschaft*, XXI (1960), 483.

36. H. König, "Ueber den Einfluss besonders niederfrquenter elektrischer Vorgänge in der Atmosphäre auf die Umwelt," *Z. f. angew. Bader- u. Klimaheilk.*, IX (1962), 481.

37. Y. Rocard, *Le signal du sourcier* (Paris: Dunod, 1962).

✦

Season of Birth

W‌HEN pregnancy comes to term, the newborn, only a fetus a moment before, separates itself from its mother; it is a moving instant in which a new man begins to live alone, to use his own lungs, to give out his first cry. The appearance of a new life on earth has always caused an understandable fascination. The act of birth is still enveloped by mysteries; it was natural for men of the past to ask: "Wasn't there something important happening in heaven at the time of my birth? Why couldn't that event have influenced the development of my life?"

The beliefs our ancestors wove around the date of birth belong to a view of the realities of this world we have outgrown. But this is not reason enough to forget the question entirely. It is more scientific to reformulate it in terms that can be answered according to contemporary knowledge. This is a challenge that several men of science have taken up. They have concluded that biological phenomena depend on a variety of cosmic rhythms. The whole cosmos, in fact, seems to be involved, from the seasonal clocks to the lunar or planetary timegivers.

Importance of the Month of Birth

The season at which people are born has far greater importance than is generally supposed. At certain seasons the number of babies is unusually large, and the proportion of girls is high. The children born at those times have a low death rate in infancy, and the survivors live to more than the average age. In addition, the births of persons who achieve distinction rise to high proportions. Such conditions indicate not only that reproduction is stimulated at certain seasons, but that children then born are more vigorous than those born at other times.[1]

These lines were written in 1938 by E. Huntington of Yale University in his work *Season of Birth, Its Relation to Human Abilities*. Even before, it had been known that seasonal clocks exercise an influence over the birth frequency at different periods of the year. In the northern hemisphere, the frequency of births is higher in May and June than in November and December. These frequencies are a function of the frequency of conception nine months earlier; that is, more conceptions take place in August and September than in February and March. Specialists did not find these results at all startling; they accounted for them in terms of seasonal conditions due to the earth's revolution around the sun. During summer vacations, for both material and psychological reasons, there are more opportunities for sexual relations than at the end of winter.

But physicians were not satisfied with this seemingly obvious explanation. They wondered whether seasonal fluctuations in hormone secretions that favor procreation might not account even better for the birth rhythm. In 1922, Dr. Abels of Vienna observed that the birth weights of children born in that city in the summer were two hundred grams more, on the average, than the weights of children born in the winter. The larger children seemed to have been conceived during the season most favorable for procreation.[2] Our own recent research into the birth weights of thousands of infants born in the Department of Seine, France, showed similar results. Abels' finding supported the hypothesis of rhythms in hormone secretions involved in pregnancy.

Month of Birth and Body Build

In 1938, Huntington phrased a bold question: Does the month in which a child is born serve as an indication of the child's future constitution? First, he collected tens of thousands of birth dates to study the relationship between these and the length of life. This research allowed him to conclude:

> Among the people who are now born at the most favorable season, the average duration of life is several years longer than among those born at the least favorable season. This is true even in comparatively good climates like that of the northern United States. It is probably true to a still greater degree in countries like Japan. . . . Length of life is of course dependent upon many factors beside the season at which one is born. Pearl (1934) has shown that long life is hereditary. . . . Mode of life has also a great influence upon how long people live. . . . But all this does not alter the fact that in the past, in New England, for example, the people born in March, and attaining at least the age of 2 years, have lived on an average nearly 4 years longer than similar people born in July. Length of life depends

upon the combined effect of many causes; the investigations here described show that season of birth must be added to the causes already known.[3]

After World War II the British demographer Fitt published a report on twenty-one thousand New Zealand recruits whose weight and height data were available. He discovered the following relationship between the month of birth and the size of the soldiers:

> The larger men were born in February [summer in the southern hemisphere], and the smaller ones in June [which is winter down under]; the heaviest ones were born in December, although the difference in weight was relatively less important than the difference in height.[4]

Month of Birth and Intelligence

According to Pinter, a child's month of birth is related to his future intellectual abilities. In 1933, he

> tabulated the intelligence quotients of thousands of school children in or near New York. He found that on an average the children born in May and June and also in September and October have a slightly higher IQ than those born at other seasons. Among the 17,000 children whom he investigated, the average intelligence quotient was lowest among those born in January and February.[5]

More recently, another American psychologist, Florence Goodenough, observed a slight edge in intelligence quotients for schoolchildren born in summer months, as against those born in the winter. According to Clarence Mills, children in Cincinnati who were born during the summer had twice as good a chance to pass college entrance examinations as those born in winter. The British psychologist J.E. Orme has studied the question with adults.[6] He compared two groups: one consisted of institutionalized mentally defective people, the other of "super-normal" members of "Mensa," a club that accepts only people with I.Q.'s over 149.

Pinter again, and later Petersen, collected several thousand birthdates of famous people from *American Men of Science* and the *Who's Who*.[7] It appears that the month of birth is related to whether one will become in the future a person "of highest eminence." This is also Huntington's opinion: "The data support the idea that season of birth bears a close relation with genius and eminence. . . . Genius apparently arises from a fortunate combination of the genes within the chromosomes at the time of conception."[8]

In 1957, H. Knobloch and B. Pasamanick did a study at the lower extremity of the intellectual scale. Their research involved computing the birthdates of mentally handicapped children at the Columbus State School born between 1913 and 1948.[9] The distribution of births is not uniform across the year, and it differs from that of the American population as a whole during the same period. The winter months of January, February, and March had a significantly larger proportion of births than the summer months. The authors found only 1,297 retarded children who were born in August, as opposed to 1,507 born in the month of February.

Sauvage-Nolting, a Dutch psychiatrist, conducted an extensive survey on the month of birth of 2,090 schizophrenics.[10] Of these, 628 were born during the three winter months (January to March), while only 428 were born in summer (July to September). Similar findings were reported for children suffering from certain types of epilepsy, some reading defects, tics, and behavioral disorders. They all suggest that the season of a child's birth is not independent of the physical and mental aptitudes that appear later in life.

How can such findings be explained? The general consensus is that seasonal clocks, through climatic factors, can affect both the course of pregnancy and the first months after birth either favorably or unfavorably. It must be emphasized that the trends reported above, while being statistically significant, do not imply any rigid determinism on behavior. In no way do they justify the astrologers' claims on the influences of the signs of the zodiac, which do not even correspond to the months of the year.

A Twenty-four-hour Rhythm of Birth

The Belgian statistician Quetelet had noticed as far back as the nineteenth century that children are not born at the same rate throughout the twenty-four hours of the day. Every author who has studied this problem has confirmed this finding. The efforts of Goehlert and Jenny in Switzerland; Kirchhoff in Germany; Charles in Great Britain; Somogyi in Italy; Points, King, Kaiser, and Halberg in the U.S.;[11] Malek in Czechoslovakia;[12] and our own work in France[13, 14] have made it possible to describe with precision the circadian clock* that regulates the hour of birth. The peak in births occurs toward the end of the night and the first hours of the day; the trough in

* Circadian, from the Latin *circa* (around) and *dies* (day). It is a word created by the specialists as a substitute for "diurnal" or "daily." The length of the night and of the day is continually changing, and it is the constant sum of the two that is relevant here.

the first hours of the afternoon. This rhythm, which has been observed since time immemorial, is now being changed by the action of newly developed drugs that affect the natural birth process.

The circadian clock also gives the time for the onset of labor. The works of Charles and Malek and our studies show that labor pains begin twice as often at midnight as at noon:[15] it is at midnight that the mother's body is most relaxed. The hour at which the child is born can also serve, to a certain extent, as an indication of his future vitality. Dr. Malek finds that natural deliveries begun at the most favorable time, that is, around midnight, are the fastest and easiest ones. The twenty-four-hour rhythm, our most powerful timegiver, imposes its schedule on the female organism and controls its nervous and hormone activities. This is the nature of the causation that seems to regulate the processes of birth.

The Great Midwife?

From antiquity the moon has been held to exert a favorable influence on births; in some parts of the earth it was called "the great midwife." Recently, several physicians wanted to see whether there was a true relationship between the number of births and the best known lunar cycles: the lunar month and the lunar day.

Let us first review the work done on the lunar month, which consists of the moon's passage through its four phases. The researchers compared these phases with a considerable number of birth statistics before reaching their conclusions; for instance, Drs. Menaker and Menaker collected information on more than half a million births that occurred in New York City hospitals between 1948 and 1957. This huge investigation, conducted with the utmost care, allowed them to reach the following conclusion: There are more births during the waning moon than during the waxing moon, with a maximum just after the full moon and a minimum after the new moon. This trend, although slight, is extremely significant because of the large sample used.[16]

This result appears to confirm the truth of the old empirical assertions. Yet other researchers have found different results; it could be said, in fact, that the main characteristic of the research on this question is the inconsistency of the various conclusions. Notwithstanding the fact that sufficiently large samples and appropriate methods were used, the results contradict each other. For example, Curtis Jackson, controller of the Methodist Hospital of Southern California, has found that "of the babies born at that hospital during the time covered (1939–1944), 17% more were born during the waxing period of the moon than during the waning period of the moon."[17] This result contradicts the one obtained by the Menakers. Several German researchers have dealt with the issue, and most of them found no relationship between phases of the moon and number of births. Among these were Kirchhoff and Fischer, who in 1939 worked with 50,000 cases, and Hosemann and Nottbohm, who used 27,000 cases ten years later.[18] The scientist therefore has to wait for more agreement in the results before accepting the existence of an effect of the lunar phases on variations in birthrate. Also, the nature of this effect will have to be explained.

The contradictions between the results obtained so far may have been because the researchers were working at widely separated locations. Some undeniable lunar influences, like the ones acting on the tides, manifest themselves in different—sometimes opposite—ways depending on geographical location. In New York City, for example, there are two daily tides at regular intervals; in

San Francisco the two tides are so close together that the ebb of the first meets the flow of the second; and in Pensacola, Florida, there is only one tide each day.

Birth and the Lunar Day

We know that the tides depend on the daily rotation of the earth in relation to the moon. This fact has engendered beliefs that are as old as the ones related to lunar phases; for instance, the people on the shores of the North Sea claim that children are born more often when the tide flows than when it ebbs. In 1947, a German physician on the Island of Norderney, Dr. Schultze, attempted to test this belief. He combed the birth registers of the island and recorded all the births that took place at the high tide and at the low tide. He found that the two numbers were equal, and concluded that the popular notion lacked any foundation.[19]

A few years later, Dr. Kirchhoff conducted a similar investigation in the same region. He too found no excess of births during the flowing tide.[20] But Kirchhoff went further and studied also the breakdown of birth frequencies as a function of the tide's age. Thus he discovered that an unusually large number of births occurred just at the time of the high tide.[21] In other words, there was a sudden increase in births each day when the moon passed over the local meridian—when, in astronomical language, the moon was "culminating." This raised the question of whether it was the moon, rather than the tides, that caused the change in the frequency of births. It was in some ways a question similar to the one Brown asked himself when he studied the time of the opening of the oyster's shell. The answers were also extraordinarily similar: as with the animals studied by Brown, the biological clock controlling uterine contractions seemed to be set to the time of the moon's passage overhead.

Another German physician, Dr. Günther, obtained results analogous to those of Kirchhoff. In studying the birthrate of the city of Cologne, far from the sea and from the tides, he found an increase of births at the culmination of the moon. Although his co-worker Harfst could not find any linkage between the moon and the births in the city of Kiel, Kirchhoff thought that his observations dealt with an interesting phenomenon, one that could suggest an important discovery. Instead of disguising the similarity between his findings and the old popular beliefs, Dr. Kirchhoff tried to explain how it happens that a popular tradition can discover the existence of a fact without being completely conscious of it or without completely understanding it:

> The daily life of the seaboard people of the North Sea is strongly influenced by the pulse of the tides. It is not difficult to see that their awareness of an association between frequent births and the high tide would develop into a firm rule. This must have occurred gradually, through a great many generations. But they never became conscious of the fact that the tides are only a side-effect of the moon's position relative to the earth. For the people living inland, the culmination of the moon means very little; so they never developed an awareness of the relationship. We know today that the oceans are not alone in being influenced by the moon's attraction; the continental masses and the atmosphere are also affected. If there are terrestrial and atmospheric tides, it is possible to hope that "lunar influences" will eventually be traced to perfectly understandable causes. Thus they will lose their "occult flavor," and become smoothly integrated into the body of scientific knowledge.[22]

NOTES TO CHAPTER TEN

1. E. Huntington, *Season of Birth, Its Relation to Human Abilities* (New York: John Wiley, 1938).
2. M. Gauquelin, "Contribution à l'étude de la variation saisonnière du poids des enfants à la naissance," *Population*, No. 3 (1967), p. 544.
3. Huntington, *op. cit.*
4. A. Reinberg and J. Ghata, *Rythmes et cycles biologiques* (Paris: P.U.F., 1957).
5. Huntington, *op. cit.*
6. J. Orme, "Ability and Season of Birth," *British Journal of Psychology*, LVI (1965), 471.
7. W. Petersen, *The Patient and the Weather* (Chicago: 1934), Vol. III.
8. Huntington, *op. cit.*
9. H. Knobloch and B. Pasamanick, "Seasonal Variation in the Birth of the Mentally Deficient," *American Journal of Public Health,* XLVIII (1958), 1201.
10. Sauvage-Nolting, "Relation entre le mois de naissance et .la schizophrenie," *Ned. Tijdschr. Geseensk.,* XCV (1951), 3855.
11. I. Kaiser and F. Halberg, "Circadian Periodic Aspects of Birth," *Annals of the New York Academy of Science,* XCVIII (1962), 1056.
12. J. Malek, J. Gleich, and V. Maly, "Characteristics of the Daily Rhythm of Menstruation and Labor," *Annals of the New York Academy of Science,* XCVIII (1962), 1042.
13. M.F. Gauquelin, "L'heure de la naissance," *Population,* IV (1959), 683.
14. ———, "L'heure de la naissance," *Le Concours Médical,* XXV (1959), 3241; XXVI (1960), 3371.
15. M. Gauquelin, "Note sur le rythme journalier du début du travail de l'accouchement," *Gynécologie et Obstétrique,* LXVI (1967), No. 2, 229.
16. W. and A. Menaker, "Lunar Periodicity in Human Reproduction," *American Journal of Obstetrical Gynecology,* LXXVII (1959), 905.

17. E. Dewey, "The Moon as a Cause of Cycles," *Cycles*, X (1959), No. 9, 197.

18. H. Hosemann, "Bestehen solare und lunare Einflüsse auf die Nativität und den Menstruationszyklus?" *Z. f. Geburtshilfe u. Gynäkol.*, CXXXIII (1950), No. 3, 263.

19. K. Schultze, "Beeinflussen Flut und Ebbe den Geburtseintritt?" *Deut. Med. Wochschr.* (1949), 311.

20. H. Kirchhoff, "Unterliegt der Wehenbeginn kosmischen Einflüssen," *Zb. f. Gynäk.*, III (1935), 135.

21. ———, "Umweltfaktoren und Genitalfunktionem," *Geburtsh. u. Frauenh.*, VI (1939), 377.

22. *Ibid.*

Planets and Heredity

$\mathbb{B}$ACON compares scientific investigation to a hunt; the observations one chances upon are the game. To continue his comparison, one could say that while the game may be found after a long search, it can also be found when one isn't looking for it at all, or when one is looking for a different animal altogether."[1] This quotation from the great French physiologist Claude Bernard seems to explain a strange incident in our scientific adventure: we began to track one kind of a game in our statistical computations, and ended up one day by catching a very different one in our nets.

Around 1950, as we were preparing our critique of traditional astrology (cf. Chapter Six), we found ourselves confronted, somewhat unwillingly, with a strange result. In one of our research samples—composed of the birth dates of 576 members of the French Academy of Medicine—the frequency of the position of certain planets was altogether unusual. The phenomenon did not correspond to any of the traditional laws of astrology, but it was interesting, nevertheless. What we had observed was that a large number of future great physicians were born when the planets Mars and Saturn had just risen or culminated in the sky.[2]

The Medical Stars

Because of the daily rotation of the earth on its own axis, the planets—just like the sun—appear to rise in the east, climb up in the sky until they reach a peak or culmination point, then descend and eventually set in the west. This is their daily movement; thus we have not only solar days and lunar days, but also Venusian days, Martian days, and so on.

Let us consider the daily motion of the planet Mars. The astronomical yearbooks tell us when Mars will rise or set each day. Let's assume that on a given day in New York, Mars rises at 0 h. 44 m. P.M. and culminates at 5 h. 33 m. P.M. If a child is born at 1:00 P.M. that day, Mars will be just rising at his birth; and if he is born at 6:00 P.M., Mars will be culminating at his birth. At each birth, the ten celestial bodies of the solar system occupy a different position in space, and it is easy to locate their position with the help of the astronomical yearbooks.

What made the phenomenon observed with the famous members of the Academy of Medicine especially singular was that it did not occur with all persons. We compared it with a sample of normal individuals selected at random from official census records. The normal subjects were not born more frequently when Mars and Saturn rose or culminated; that is, the planetary clocks did not work the same way with the famous physicians as they did with the average person. The inexplicable phenomenon was embarrassing to us; we decided not to question its meaning too closely, but rather to repeat the investigation and see whether the bizarre relationship would repeat itself. We thus assembled a second sample of 508 eminent physicians. The work involved was not simple; we had to find not only the names of these doctors but also the date and locality of their births; then we had to write to the mayors of their home towns to obtain the exact time of birth. This precision was necessary because the planets change their positions hour by hour, as a function of the daily rotation of the earth; it was also necessary to conduct this work on the most solid demographical and astronomical base, to avoid erroneous conclusions. But all this is a different story, which is related in sufficient detail in a methodological work.[3]

At the end of our second study, the evidence reproduced itself with stubborn insistence: as in the first group, the birth dates of the famous physicians clustered after the rise or the culmination of Mars and Saturn. An undeniable statistical correlation appeared between the rise and culmination of these planets at the child's birth and his future success as a doctor.

The Schedule of Success

This strange fact obviously required further examination in depth. As a consequence, we expanded our study to include the birthdates of every famous Frenchman we were able to find.[4,5] Then we visited the libraries and civic records of several foreign countries: in 1956 we were in Italy, in 1957 in Germany, in 1958 in Belgium and Holland; in this way we collected more than 25,000 birthdates, including not only those of doctors, but also of writers, actors, politicians, athletes, military men, etc.

As we continued to compute the planetary positions at the moment of birth, the strange pattern persisted instead of disappearing. Eventually, a more and more precise statistical relationship appeared between time of birth and professional career. The physicians were not the only ones involved; each group seemed to have a planetary clock of its own. And Mars and Saturn were not the only planetary timegivers; Jupiter and the moon appeared to be just as important for other professional men. Each time, the statistical anomalies showed themselves just after the rise and the culmination of the planet. For instance, a great many individuals born when Mars was appearing over the horizon or passing at the highest point of its course later became famous doctors, great athletes, or military leaders, while future artists, painters, or musicians were seldom born at the times propitious for doctors and athletes. Actors and politicians were born more frequently when Jupiter rose or culminated—but scientists were rarely born at that time. Thus, as far as vocational success was concerned, the moon, Mars, Jupiter, and Saturn were found to act as planetary clocks (*see* Figs. 7a and 7b). A cosmic pulsation seemed to cause, during the twenty-four-hour cycle of the day, more births of future doctors at certain times, more future artists at others, and so on. Table II gives a summary of our observations, as they were reported in 1960 with an introduction by Dr. Bender, Professor of Psychology at the University of Freiburg in Breisgau.[6, 7]

Looking for an Explanation

Our work deeply perplexed many astronomers, demographers, and statisticians. On the one hand, they found no objections to our methodology; on the other, they refused to concede that a relationship so close to old astrological beliefs could exist. After recognizing our conclusions, the scientific community raised a number of pertinent questions that had to be answered. How could

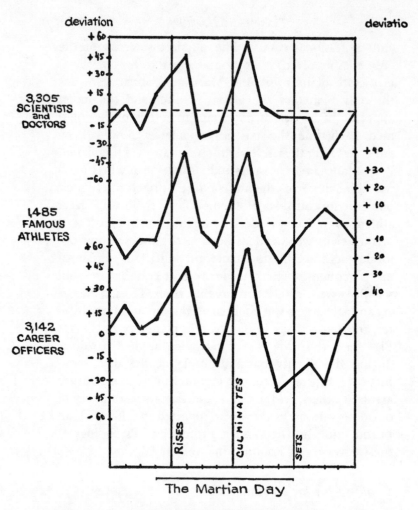

Fig. 7a—*The Martian Clock and Successful Vocations*
A very large number of children born when Mars either rises or culminates later become famous scientists, physicians, athletes, or career
officers in the armed services. On the abscissa, the diurnal movement of
Mars, divided into sectors; on the ordinate, the difference between expected and observed frequencies. These differences are highly significant
(*see* Appendix I). Similarly surprising results were obtained with the
moon, Jupiter and Saturn. (After M. Gauquelin, *Les Hommes et les
Astres* [Paris: Denoel, 1960].)

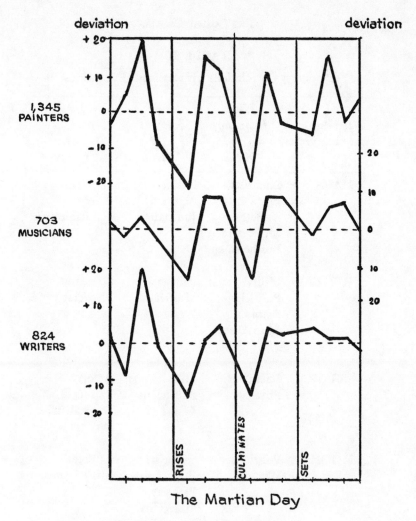

Fig. 7b—*The Martian Clock and Successful Vocations*
A very small number of children born when Mars either rises or culminates later become famous painters, musicians, or writers. On the abscissa, the diurnal movement of Mars divided in sectors. On the ordinate, the difference between expected and observed frequencies. These differences are highly significant (*see* Appendix I). (After M. Gauquelin, *Les Hommes et les Astres* [Paris: Denoel, 1960].)

TABLE II

Planetary Correlations with Successful Vocations

After rise and culmination of*	High frequency of births	Average frequency of births	Low frequency of births
MARS	Scientists Physicians Athletes Military men Businessmen	Politicians Actors Journalists	Writers Painters Musicians
JUPITER	Military men Politicians Actors Journalists Playwrights	Painters Musicians Writers	Scientists Physicians
SATURN	Scientists Physicians	Military men Politicians	Actors Painters Journalists Writers
MOON	Politicians Writers	Scientists Physicians Painters Musicians Journalists	Athletes Military men

(After M. Gauquelin, *Les Hommes et les Astres* (Paris: Denoël, 1960), p. 200.)

* For the astronomical definition of the rising and culminating sectors, *see* Appendix I.

classical physics account for the statistical relationship? What interaction is possible between the child being born and the rise or culmination of a given planet? Why would Mars act differently from Jupiter?

In other words, we somehow had to integrate our peculiar planetary effects into the total picture of modern science. The problem was, how could this be done? One possibility is that some form of radiation issuing from the planets marks the newborn at birth with an influence whose effect persists the whole life long. Let us take an example: If a child is born when Mars is rising, we could assume that the planet exerts a sudden action that modifies the child's organism. After this action, the child would have "something more" than his parents gave him through heredity. And this "something more" would have sufficiently strong and lasting influences to result in the child's having specific gifts and a definite orientation toward his existence.

Of course, one cannot entertain this idea seriously. When the child is born, his coming into the world is the completion of nine months of gestation, during which his organism is completely developed. One could perhaps suppose that some action influencing the arrangement of the chromosomes might take place at conception, but such action at birth seems indeed unbelievable. It is then too late to influence the hereditary temperament of the child. Besides, one would have to postulate the existence of a mysterious energy, which the planets do not seem to possess. The obvious answer thus appears too simple, too close to astrology itself, to be of any use. Are there, then, alternative answers? That is the real question.

Variable Levels of Sensitivity

There is another possibility. A simple illustration will help explain it: the effects of solar radiation on the skin. If two individuals, one a blonde and the other a brunette, sunbathe on a beach for the same length of time, the skin of the former will burn while the latter's will only tan. The reason for this difference is simple: because of hereditary dissimilarity, the two persons respond with individual variations in sensitivity to the ultraviolet radiation of the sun. This example of the sun's action is pretty obvious and may not seem applicable to our purpose. Fortunately, however, there are other observations that can provide useful support.

One of the observations made by Dr. Takata, whose work was discussed in Chapter Nine, is that the rise and descent of human blood serum indices show a changing threshold of sensitivity to solar action not equally distributed in the population.[8] An even more interesting theory for our purposes is the one advanced in 1946 by the biometeorologist M. Curry, according to which there are individual differences in responses to atmospheric conditions.[9] Curry found two general types of reactions to the weather: the "K" and the "W." The "K's" are people who are very sensitive to the lowering of temperature. They are usually thin and long-faced; temperamentally they are introverted. The "W's", on the other hand, are extroverted, active, and dynamic; their bodies are rather heavy, and they suffer when the temperature increases suddenly.

Such variable levels of sensitivity to outside conditions have also been observed among animals. In 1955, J. Aschoff of the Max Planck Institute in Germany noted that mice living in identically lighted environments followed different cycles of activity. In 1962 Brown and Terracini studied the behavior of mice placed in uniform experimental conditions. They found that there was a relationship between the animals' activity and the lunar day, but that each animal had its own way of following the cosmic clock. They concluded that the differences may be due to individual genetic heredity.[10] Thus, the hereditary constitution of each individual seems to mediate the action of the cosmic clocks. In the words of G. Piccardi, "Two individuals belonging to the same species but having different genetic makeups will not react the same way to external events. On the other hand, those who share the same heredity will react in identical fashion."[11]

A Genetic Theory

Thus the newborn's heredity, rather than a sudden action emanating from the planets, might account for our findings. Perhaps, at the time of birth, each child manifests an inherited sensitivity to planetary clocks. "We could," says Piccardi,

> envision a planetary action which affects the onset of labor, but does not modify the constitution of the individual who is being born. Thus the action would be temporary, affecting only the process of birth, without leaving any traces on the organism. The organism of the child is controlled by the laws of heredity; and it is possible, because of these laws, that it will be sensitive to the action of the celestial bodies exactly in the same way that his parents were at their birth. The crisis of birth, already gathering itself, would unfold when all the favorable conditions have been attained; among these, the planets might have their role.[12]

This would mean that the birth of a child when Mars appears over the horizon is not mere chance. The birth occurs at that moment rather than another because his organism is ready to react to the perturbations caused by this particular planet at its passage over the horizon. In other words, the position of a planet at a child's birth might be linked to his heredity. This idea is the exact opposite of astrological predestination because "it would mean that the action of the celestial body would not be fixed forever into the organism of the newborn; it would only have a temporary effect during childbirth."[13]

The following hypothesis can be proposed: The child inherits from his parents a tendency to be born when Mars rises, in the same way he inherits the color of his hair. In order to confirm the hypothesis, the research had to demonstrate that the child's parents had also shown this tendency, in other words, that they also were born at the time of Mars's appearance. The task then was to collect a group of parents who were born when Mars was rising and observe whether their children were also born more often when the planet occupied the same position in the sky:

> To prove the existence of planetary heredity, one needs to demonstrate statistically that there are similarities between the position of the planets at the parents' birth and that of their children. We worked for more than five years on the birth records of several counties in the Paris region, and assembled data on more than thirty thousand parents and their children. When the data were submitted to a statistical analysis, the magnitude of the hereditary similarity was so large that it could not be attributed to chance. To be exact, there was only one chance in half a million that the results were random; or 499,999 chances to one that planetary heredity was indeed real.[14]

An important qualification must be appended to this statement: The similarities were found only for the celestial bodies closest to the earth or largest in mass. Only the moon, Venus, Mars, Jupiter, and Saturn were found at

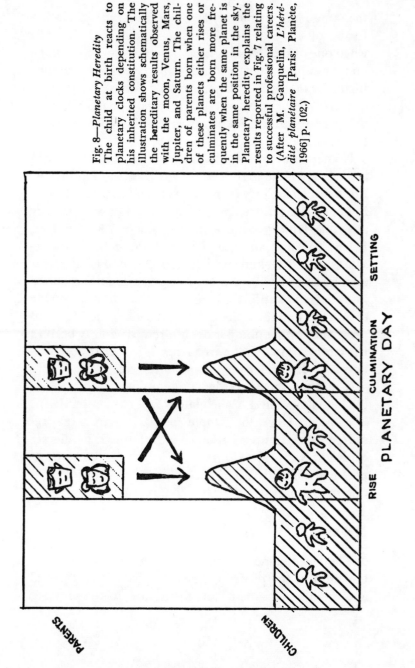

Fig. 8—*Planetary Heredity*
The child at birth reacts to planetary clocks depending on his inherited constitution. The illustration shows schematically the hereditary results observed with the moon, Venus, Mars, Jupiter, and Saturn. The children of parents born when one of these planets either rises or culminates are born more frequently when the same planet is in the same position in the sky. Planetary heredity explains the results reported in Fig. 7 relating to successful professional careers.
(After M. Gauquelin, *L'hérédité planétaire* [Paris: Plancte, 1966] p. 102.)

PARENTS

CHILDREN

RISE   CULMINATION   SETTING

PLANETARY DAY

the same place in the sky at birth from one generation to the other. Children have the tendency to be born when one of these bodies rises or culminates, if the same body occupied that region of the sky at their parents' birth.[15] These same planets, except Venus, are also the ones connected with successful careers. Apparently, these five planets can indeed be called the timegivers of birth (*see* Figs. 8 and 9).

No hereditary result was obtained for Mercury, which is small and close to the sun; or for Uranus, Neptune, or Pluto, which are very far removed from the earth. At least in our investigations, these planets did not seem to play any timegiving role on birth. The relationship between hereditary effect and the planets' distance-mass ratio reminds us of well-known physical laws (*see* Fig. 10). It is also in accord with the laws of genetics and scientific knowledge about birth. The sex of the parent or of the child does not affect the pattern, nor does the length of pregnancy or the number of children previously born to the mother. Finally, the frequency is higher if both parents are born under the same planetary position.

There are, however, some circumstances under which the hereditary effect of the planets fails to manifest itself. This occurs when the sample consists of births that required surgical intervention or were induced by the use of drugs. Such cases do not conform to the pattern expected when births occur naturally; but this, of course, is one of those exceptions that confirm the rule.

Magnetic Influences

There is one more comparison to make: that between the effect of the planetary clocks we have just reviewed and the other cosmic factors mentioned in the previous

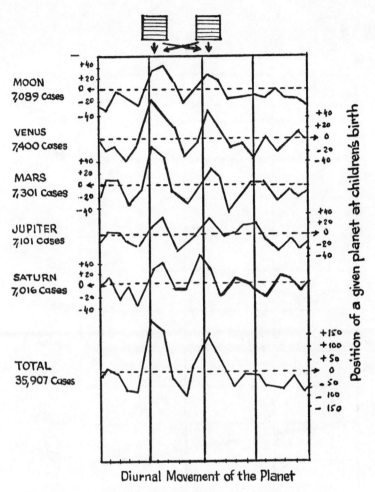

Fig. 9—*The Effects of the Five Planet Clocks on Heredity*
The graph expands the illustrative model in Fig. 8. The moon, Venus, Mars, Jupiter, and Saturn tend to occupy positions at the child's birth similar to the ones they occupied when the child's parents were born. Therefore, children are born more often at the rise or culmination of a planet if the same planet was in the same position at their parents' birth. On the abscissa, the diurnal movement divided into sectors; on the ordinate, the difference between expected and observed frequencies. (After M. Gauquelin, *L'hérédité planétaire* [Paris: Planète, 1966].)

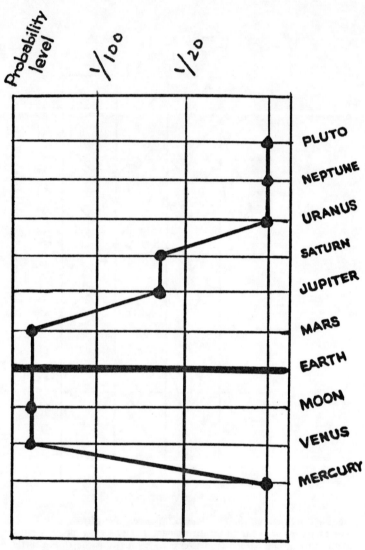

Fig. 10—*The Effect of Heredity as a Function of the Planets' Distance from Earth.*

On the abscissa, the planets aligned in the order of their distance from the earth; on the ordinate, the levels of probability reached by the statistical test, Chi-square. Only the five planets close to earth give statistically significant results. (After M. Gauquelin, *L'hérédité planétaire* [Paris: Planète, 1966], p. 100.)

chapters. For instance, does the magnetic sense, which, as we saw, exists in man as well as in animals, interfere with the planetary effects on the newborn? We felt encouraged to ask this question after Reiter[16] and Cyran[17] published their works reporting an increase of births during magnetic storms.

We took our sample of birthdates and compared, day by day, the effect of planetary heredity with geomagnetic disturbances—which, as we know, are due to solar activity. The results of this study were presented in 1966 at the Fourth International Congress of Biometeorology.[18] They show a clear, direct relationship between magnetic variations and the effects of planetary heredity;[19] if a child is born on a disturbed day, the number of hereditary similarities is twice as high as on quiet days. This suggests that the moon and the planets do affect life, through the solar field.*

The Child and Uniform Conditions

Just ten years ago the idea that a child about to be born could be so sensitive to the cosmos would have seemed unbelievable. The child in the womb may be a little cramped, but, like an astronaut in his space capsule, he appears to be well protected against the effects of all external events. It is at this point that Brown's discoveries have greatly helped us to understand what may be happening. Certainly, the child inside the maternal womb is protected against violent external changes. He lives there under uniform conditions, sheltered from such

* In 1967 we presented our results to two international scientific meetings, the Ninth International Conference of Biometeorology at Wiesbaden, Germany, and the Fourteenth Congress on Health at Ferrara, Italy.

"obvious" timegivers as light, temperature, and humidity. These factors are practically invariable for him; the child floats in complete darkness inside the amniotic liquid at a constant temperature of thirty-seven degrees Centigrade. But Brown's fundamental discovery was that living things cannot live *without* timegivers. If they are placed outside the reach of the "obvious" timegivers in the environment, they will instinctively find other patterns by which to regulate their biological rhythms, becoming most sensitive to the influence of "subtle synchronizers" from space.

It is in such a situation that the child finds itself before birth. He appears to be able to perceive extremely small changes in the cosmic environment and thus cause labor, which has been prepared for a long time in advance by progressive modifications in the bodies of the mother and the child, to begin. When term is approaching, "an infinitesimal amount of hormone in the blood is enough to produce childbirth," as J.D. Ratcliff writes.[20] It is possible that a cosmic stimulus, even one of extremely small energy, may produce such minute hormonal secretion; the progress of modern medicine makes this hypothesis feasible. Recently A. Csapo of the Rockefeller Institute, New York, demonstrated the role of placentary hormones in labor. Because the placenta and the fetus both originate in the same cell, the fetus can, through the placenta, influence the mother's uterine contractions.[21]

Toward a Practical Application

It is easier now to understand the meaning of the apparently inconceivable finding that links a person's future success in a given career to the position of a particular planet at his birth. The most convincing explanation has nothing mysterious or occult about it. Very simply, the child's career depends on the genetic structure of his organism; at birth, the planetary clocks reveal this genetic factor in an unforeseen way. The successful professionals had certain elements in their genes that allowed their lives to develop naturally in a favored direction, inherited from their parents. Of course, this relationship does not apply only to celebrities, it applies to everyone. In the human species, the inherited tendency to be born at a given hour instead of another should to a certain extent be an indication of the individual's constitutional type.

We have already seen that several rhythms act on the human organism. It appears now that there are even more subtle rhythms whose actions depend on the individual's inherited temperament; such is the influence of the planetary clocks that initiate childbirth. In explaining the mechanism of the biological clocks, we have said that some scientists support the theory of "endogenous rhythms" while others believe in "exogenous rhythms." The former, of which Halberg is a representative, emphasize the individual genetic makeup. The latter, among whom is Brown, emphasize the effect of the geophysical environment. What we have called "planetary heredity" seems to indicate that both these views contain a part of the truth. There is no doubt about the external actions of space, but they still have to filter through the internal genetic constitution.

There may be a more important consequence of planetary inheritance, one that may lead to an unexpected practical application. On the basis of the planetary clocks' position at birth, it seems possible to develop a forecast of the individual's future temperament and social behavior. When the childbirth is natural, the forecast

could be quite important—it opens up numerous possi-
bilities in medicine, biology, and psychology. It is still too
early to be sure how well the promise will be fulfilled;
the work is just beginning. What is already clear—and
this is rather important—is that the infinitely varied human reactions to the cosmos seem to fall into five general
categories. These categories are apparently related to the
five "planet clocks": the moon, Venus, Mars, Jupiter, and
Saturn. For instance, those who will become great physicians, outstanding athletes, or famous soldiers all show a
positive reaction to Mars; the ones who will become actors or politicians react positively to Jupiter; and so on.

With the help of studies in planetary inheritance there
is a strong hope of developing a fundamental classifica-
tion of human types based on a comprehensive synthesis
of the genetic biotype. In other words, planetary heredity
seems to point the way to a scientific study of individual
destiny.

In conclusion, we quote a passage by Arne Sollberger,
Secretary of the Society for Biological Rhythm Research,
that summarizes the issue with objectivity and wisdom:

> Gravitation and magnetism are dependent on the
> position of distant celestial objects. Why, that's almost
> astrology. . . . Clearly, we must be careful in accepting
> such statements but also in rejecting them because of
> the negative associations they carry in our minds. The
> problem constitutes perhaps one of the most fascinat-
> ing challenges to the biological scientist of today.[22]

NOTES TO CHAPTER ELEVEN

1. C. Bernard, *Introduction à l'étude de la médecine expérimentale* (Paris: 1856).
2. M. and F. Gauquelin, *Méthodes pour étudier la répartition des astres dans le mouvement diurne* (Paris: 1957).
3. *Ibid.*
4. M. Gauquelin, *L'influence des astres* (Paris: Le Dauphin, 1955).
5. ———, "Der E influss der Gestirne und die Statistik," *Z. f. Parapsych. u. Grenzgeb. Psychol.*, I (1957), 23.
6. ———, *Les hommes et les astres,* with a preface by Professor H. Bender (Paris: Denoël, 1960).
7. ———, "Neue Untersuchungen über den Einfluss der Gestirne," *Z. f. Parapsychol. u. Grenzgeb. Psychol.*, III (1959), 10.
8. M. Takata and T. Murasugi, "Flockungszahlstörungen im gesunden menschlichen Serum, 'kosmoterrestrischer Sympathismus,'" *Bioklimat. Beibl.*, VIII (1941), 17.
9. M. Curry, *Bioklimatik* (Riederau, 1946), two volumes.
10. E. Terracini and F.A. Brown, Jr., "Periodisms in Mouse 'Spontaneous' Activity Synchronized with Major Geophysical Cycles," *Physiological Zoology*, XXXV (1962), No. 1, 27.
11. M. Gauquelin, *L'hérédité planétaire,* with a preface by Professor G. Piccardi (Paris: Planète, 1966).
12. *Ibid.*
13. *Ibid.*
14. ———, "Die planetare Heredität," *Z. f. Parapsych. u. Grenzgeb. Psychol.*, V (1961), 168.
15. ———, "Note sur le rythme journalier du début du travail de l'accouchement," *Gynécologie et Obstétrique*, LXVI (1967), No. 2, 231.
16. R. Reiter, "Wetter und Zahl der Geburten," *Dtch. Med. Wochenschr.*, LXXVII (1952), 1606.
17. W. Cyran, "Ueber die biologische Wirksamkeit solarer Vorgänge (nachgewiesen am Wehenbeginn)," *Geburtshilfe u. Frauenheilk,* X (1950), 667.

18. M. and F. Gauquelin, *A Possible Hereditary Effect on Time of Birth in Relation to the Diurnal Movement of the Moon and the Nearest Planets, Its Relationship with Geomagnetic Activity* (Amsterdam: Swets and Zeitlinger, 1967).
19. ———, "L'effet planétaire d'hérédité et le magnétisme terrestre," *Z. f. Parapsychol. u Grenzgeb. d. Psychol.*, IX (1967), No. 1.
20. J. Ratcliff, *La Naissance* (Paris: Stock, 1953).
21. A. Csapo, "Function and Regulation of the Myometrium," *Annals of the New York Academy of Science*, CXV (1959), No. 2, 780.
22. A. Sollberger, *Biological Rhythm Research* (New York: Elsevier, 1965).

The Fluid of Life

T HE FOLLOWING scene takes place in a chemical laboratory. An assistant, holding a vial in his hands, is losing his patience. The chemical reaction that usually occurs very rapidly is not happening today. Yet the lab assistant knows his job; as usual, he weighed the ingredients carefully before mixing them in the container; he washed the vial with the greatest care; he used water twice distilled—in short, he took all the precautions needed for the success of the experiment. But nothing helps. So he goes to consult his professor, who answers with a shrug: "It is chance; let's forget it." They agree to classify the case with the "aberrant reactions" and wait until later in the day, or the week, to repeat the experiment in the hope that everything will return to normal.

In theory, when one mixes two chemical substances in a test tube, if one is careful to use the same method each time, the same reaction will always take place. But this only happens in theory. In reality, each reaction has its idiosyncrasies. Its speed changes from day to day. Sometimes it does not appear at all. All chemists know of such abnormalities, but, at least until very recently, they preferred not to talk about them. Piccardi writes: "Chemists have never thought that each hour might not be like every other. But if they have thought so, they have never admitted it; it would have been too dangerous."[1] Although such occurrences are commonplace, admitting them could indeed have dangerous repercussions. It would mean that chemical properties change from one hour to the next without their chemical formulas being changed. Scientists refuse to admit this enormity, which would rock the whole edifice of chemistry on its foundations. Thus the professor preferred to explain the phenomenon to his lab assistant in terms of "chance" and "aberrant" reactions.

The Freezing Point of Water

The files of chemical laboratories are filled with aberrant observations ignored and forgotten, destined to disappear sooner or later. Most such observations involve fluids, especially colloids suspended in water. Few truths seem more obvious and more certain than the statement that water freezes at thirty-two degrees Fahrenheit and changes into ice. Actually, this is often untrue. Sometimes the temperature has to be lowered far below thirty-two degrees before water turns to ice. This is the kind of aberrant reaction that ends up at the bottom of the files.

But some scientists are more curious than others. Around 1950, the German biologist H. Bortels of Berlin University became interested in this phenomenon. He investigated the strange behavior of water, which specialists call "surfusion," and he demonstrated that its causes were not random. They were affected by some well-defined, yet mysterious factors: although samples of pure water were sealed off from any external influence, the surfusion seemed to follow the variations in atmospheric pressure and in the activity of terrestrial magnetism.[2]

A few years before, Mrs. E. Findeisen had systematically studied the reaction speed of an inorganic chemical solution, arsenic trisulfide, inside sealed vials. The solution, apparently isolated from any outside influence, aged at different speeds from day to day. (To "age," in the case of a chemical solution, means to change chemically with time.) Moreover, the solution behaved differently on the upper floors of the laboratory than on the lower floors. Through thousands of measurements, Mrs. Findeisen showed that these changes depended on external factors.[3]

Bortels and Findeisen noticed in their vials the appearance of a phenomenon strangely analogous to the one observed by Brown in animals and noted in our work in children about to be born. Although enclosed inside a uniform environment, the colloids suspended in water are mysteriously informed of changes in certain external factors. Again, where does the information come from? How can it be perceived by inorganic compounds? It is hard to believe that inorganic matter could be as capricious as biological structures are.

A Parenthesis

At this point let us open a parenthesis. With chemical reactions we have finally reached the basic levels of nature. In showing that chemical elements react to cosmic events in a manner similar to that of living organisms, we are approaching a fundamental explanation. The discoveries presented before had shown us that our bodies are sensitive to the effects of extraterrestrial space. But we were still lacking information about what happens inside our bodies. We had no idea what senses are involved in the reception of the electrical, magnetic, and gravitational messages. It was not known whether these receptors function as the eye does, receiving only one set of rays, or whether each cell in the body possesses the same capacity to receive these messages. In the second hypothesis, our whole body could be seen as a giant test tube inside which chemical reactions involving every cell are taking place. J.L. Cloudsley-Thompson, a specialist in biological rhythms, writes, "The question arises as to whether such organisms *are* a clock or *contain* a clock. Perhaps this quesion should not be asked, however, at least not by a biologist."[4]

The specialists recognize that at this stage, it is the chemists' turn to speak. It is therefore important for us to understand the abnormal behavior of chemical compounds when related to outer space conditions.

Simple Witchcraft?

Professor Giorgio Piccardi, Director of the Institute for Physical Chemistry in Florence, has been especially intrigued by the scandalously aberrant behavior of laboratory reactions. In 1935 he said, "It is not a good procedure to deny something one sees only because there is no way to understand it."[5] He then decided to attack the question. At the beginning his inquiry assumed rather prosaic forms: he became interested in how to remove incrustations from boilers. Water leaves calcareous deposits inside containers used to hold it; housewives have this problem with their cooking pots, and industrial boilers are no exception. Such deposits can seriously affect the functioning of the engines, and various chemical processes are used to dissolve them. One process is to add specially treated water to the boiler at regular intervals. Piccardi describes this method as follows:

A vial of glass containing a drop of mercury and low pressure neon is slowly stirred inside the water. As the container is moved, the mercury rubs against the glass; the double electric layer between the mercury and the glass breaks and produces a red luminescent discharge through the neon. The water touching the vial ends up *activated*.[6]

Activated water not only fails to develop calcareous deposits once it is poured in a boiler, it actually dissolves prior incrustations, so that they can be drained off in the form of a muddy solution. But the chemical composition of the physically treated water remained absolutely identical to normal water. It was indeed like sorcery: a few red lights, a few electrical discharges, and *presto!* The water acquired "miraculous" properties. An alchemist of the Dark Ages could not hope to achieve more surprising results from the manipulations of his retorts and alembics. In fact, many researchers refused to admit the efficacy of this procedure. Their refusal was all the more understandable because the physiochemical action of activated water on calcareous deposits was not uniformly effective. But if chemists could remain indifferent to the inconsistencies in the reactions taking place inside their laboratories, plant owners could not afford to ignore the problems posed by boilers whose deposits would not dissolve; this is why Piccardi was called in on the scene.

Piccardi had already faced this particular question and had developed an explanation for it. In reproducing the reaction of activated water on calcareous deposits in the laboratory, he found that the variability was not due to chance—the chance modern science invokes to explain unknown phenomena the way past centuries invoked satanic forces. One day he had covered his vials with a thin metallic screen. Although this covering did not touch the activated water, its presence sufficed to modify the speed of the reaction. It seemed as if the metallic surface acted as a shield, keeping out forces coming from outside, from above. "In 1939," Piccardi writes, "I realized that the constantly fluctuating behavior of activated water depended on something happening in the space that surrounds us"[7] (*see* Fig. 11).

The Method of Chemical Tests

In order to find out more about the agents from space, Piccardi developed an original testing method. The greatest difficulty he had to cope with was the extreme variability of the reactions: how could constants be discovered in such inconsistency? Since the reactions varied from one minute to the next, what was needed was enough *simultaneous* observations to yield a statistical mean—a stable quantity unaffected by chance—and then the repetition of such simultaneous observations regularly over a period of years. Moreover, it was necessary that the reaction be simple so that the procedure could be easily standardized. Piccardi built a synchronous mixer capable of performing twenty experiments at the same time; he chose as his subject an inorganic colloid, bismuth oxychloride. The reaction consists in pouring trichloride of bismuth into distilled water, where the former precipitates. There is a great variation in the speed with which such precipitation takes place.

From 1951 on, Piccardi and his assistants measured the speed of this chemical reaction three times a day in their laboratory in Florence. The perfect continuity of these experiments, which have developed into a daily ritual, is the only hope for pinpointing the cosmic causes of daily variations. Piccardi has found an able associate

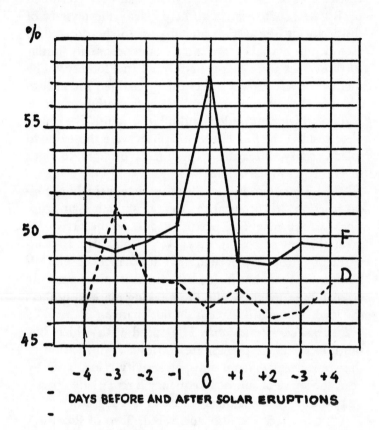

Fig. 11—*The Effects of Solar Eruptions on Chemical Reactions*
—Piccardi's "F" Test (chemical reactions performed in the open air)
---Piccardi's "D" Test (chemical reactions performed under a screen)
On the day of a solar eruption (marked O on the figure), the "F" test
shows a strong anomaly absent before and after the eruption. On the
other hand, the "D" test, which was sheltered, was not influenced by
solar eruptions. The ordinate reports the means for both tests. (After G.
Piccardi, *The Chemical Basis of Medical Climatology* [Springfield, Ill.:
Charles Thomas, 1962], p. 86.)

in Mrs. C. Capel-Boute, Director of the Electrochemical Institute at Brussels University. She had been consulted by Brussels industrialists to help clarify the mystery of disincrusting the city's water mains, so she decided to establish in her laboratories a set of experiments similar to those that were being performed in Florence.[8] The method of testing was successful. It enabled Piccardi to identify the causes of the variability that other scientists had noted without understanding its origins. The causes were cosmic: the first effects to appear were those due to solar activity. Piccardi's experiments brought to light several types of variations:

Short-Term Variations. These are changes in the chemical reaction that occur at the time of sudden solar eruptions, strong magnetic perturbations, or the arrival of great sheaves of cosmic rays. When the earth is bombarded by the effects of such sudden instances of solar ill-humor, the reactions inside beakers kept in the open air occur more quickly, while those taking place in beakers shielded by metallic screens do not change.

Eleven-Year Variations. The speed with which bismuth oxychloride precipitates varies also in relation to the eleven-year general sunspot activity cycle. Year by year, the curve of sunspot frequency is remarkably parallel to the curve of chemical reactions (*see* Fig. 12).*

A lunar effect was also uncovered. Two of Piccardi's co-workers, Papeschi and Costa, had been studying naph-

---

* There are other astonishing links between inanimate objects and the eleven-year cycle of the sun. The astronomer Barber has revealed that an electric battery installed at the Norman Lockyer Observatory at the University of Exeter had to be recharged more often during the years of greatest solar activity. From 1925 to 1960, the frequency of rechargings has faithfully followed the curve of sunspots.[9]

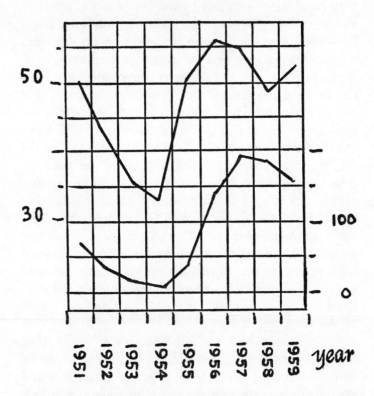

Fig. 12—*Speed of Chemical Reactions as a Function of the Eleven-Year
  Solar Cycle*
The speed with which oxychloride of bismuth precipitates is related to
sunspot activity. The upper curve reports the percentaged results for
Piccardi's chemical test through the years. The lower curve shows the
number of sunspots through the years. (After G. Piccardi, *The Chemical
Basis of Medical Climatology* [Springfield, Ill.: Charles Thomas, 1962],
p. 95.)

thalene. In 1963 they showed that its speed of solidifica-
tion was a function of the moon's phases: it was quickest
at the new moon, slowest at full moon.[10] At the same
time, the chemist A. Rima studied the effect of lunar
cycles on Piccardi's test results.[11]

In conclusion, a colloid in aqueous solution reacts to all the cosmic effects to which men and animals react. In addition, thanks to the perseverance of Piccardi's work and the ingenuity of his method, attention has been focused on the possible action of one cosmic clock that had escaped the attention of previous researchers: the earth's position in the galaxy. It is difficult to imagine how the galaxy, this universe of universes, could affect chemical reactions inside a beaker; in order to explain this possible relationship, Piccardi developed what he calls his "solar hypothesis." The earth, while turning around the sun, races across the galaxy at the dizzying speed of twelve miles per second. The course of this movement is not straight, but follows a helicoidal, screw-like path. Therefore the earth constantly changes its position with regard to the incredibly strong galactic fields of force. This is probably one or the reasons chemical reactions take place at different speeds in different months of the year.

For the years 1951 to 1961, the annual variation of Piccardi's test showed a minimum in spring, when the earth is traveling through space at the fastest rate and the only time of the year when it follows the North Pole in advance of the galaxy. In the fall, the earth's rate of speed is at its slowest. Since 1961, however, the effect of the earth's movement in the galaxy on chemical reactions could have been disturbed, according to Piccardi, by the change in relative position of the two planets Jupiter and Saturn. The disturbances are probably caused by these planets' magnetospheric tails in the solar and galactic field. Piccardi's question has been answered: conditions in space control the capricious effects of activated water on the calcareous deposits covering the walls of boilers.

The Structure of Water

Water has an odd quality that enables it to react complyingly to external influences. To understand it one has to know what water is, and it is only in the last few years that the great question mark of water has been solved. Until recently chemists, trusting appearances, assumed water to be the perfect liquid. Yet its physical properties are extremely abnormal and contradict the theoretical calculations that apply to a perfect liquid. In the words of the chemist Duval, water is "a liquid that still remembers the crystalline form of the ice from which it originates."[12]

Bernal and Fowler in 1933, and H. Frank in 1939, proposed the concept according to which water has a pseudo-crystalline structure similar to that of solid bodies.[13, 14] This means that the combination of water molecules is organized on a pattern that could not exist in a perfect liquid. Pople in 1951 advanced the hypothesis that the molecular organization was continuous, "a self-perpetuating structure"; a glass of water was, in a sense, "composed of a single molecule."[15] But this structure is extremely fragile. The pyramids of hydrogen and oxygen atoms are so tenuously linked to each other that the least external pressure can destroy the whole pattern. In comparison to the permanent structure of solids, the structure of water is unstable, subject to major changes as a result of even very low energy influences.* Even the smallest structural change will modify the physical properties of water.

* Professor H. S. Frank of the University of Pittsburgh calls these important consequences of very low energy on water "trigger-effects."

The Cosmos Upsets the Structure of Water

We have now a satisfactory solution to the problem encountered above, for we have seen that activated water has a different effect from normal water on calcareous deposits because its structure has been changed by the process of activation. If the activated water does not perform its disincrusting action on one day as well as on another, it is because cosmic factors sometimes neutralize the effects of the physical treatment. This is also why the inorganic colloids suspended in Piccardi's beakers vary so compliantly as a function of external forces. Water studied in the laboratory is as sensitive to very slight changes in electric or magnetic fields as the animals Brown studied. In 1965 two chemists at the University of Florence, Bordi and Vannel, noticed some differences in the electric conductivity of water that was exposed to the effects of a very small magnet.[16] At the National Center for Atmospheric Research of Boulder, Colorado, W.H. Fisher and his assistants have shown that the structure of water is extremely sensitive to electromagnetic fields.[17] It is through the agency of such subtle fields of force that the cosmos modifies the properties of water.

Despite its seemingly abstract nature, Piccardi's effect has vast consequences. Water is not only the liquid of our earth, it is also the liquid of our lives. Living organisms are exposed to the cosmos as the colloids in their laboratory beakers are. Cosmic forces act upon them through the mediation of the water contained in their bodies. The human body, for instance, is 65 per cent water. Water is found in blood, in the lymph, in every organ of our body. Several chemists, Magat in particular, have shown that the structure of water is especially precarious at the normal temperature of the human body. It is in fact between 35 to 40 degrees Centigrade that water definitely loses its structure to become a perfect liquid.[18]

Piccardi wrote in 1962, "Perhaps it is even by means of water and the aqueous system that the external forces are able to react on living organisms."[19] Because, he explains,

> the existence of a structure so delicate and sensitive permits the assumption that appropriate actions are capable of modifying the structure itself in an infinite number of ways, and thus we may assume that water is sensitive to extremely delicate influences and is capable of adapting itself to the most varying circumstances to a degree attained by no other liquid.[20]

Inside the human organism, as well as inside plant and animal organisms, the structure of water readily changes in response to the stimuli of outer space, whether these are waves, particles, or perturbations of a magnetic or gravitational nature. Through chemical findings, it becomes clear how living things are able to regulate their activity in response to external rhythms. Piccardi's effect explains the organism's sensitivity to such rhythms:

> We are powerless in face of external phenomena. We cannot prevent the unleashing of a magnetic storm or the eruption of sunspots; we cannot prevent very low-frequency electromagnetic waves from piercing through the walls of our laboratories, factories, homes, and bodies.[21]

All this fits very closely the thought of Brown, who in 1962 announced to the Academy of Sciences of New York:

> Physiologists must recognize that organisms, even when shielded and screened from all ordinary factors to which they have, classically, been deemed sensitive, still

are obtaining information about their rhythmic external environment on our planet.[22]

The Cosmic Basis of Life

Only recently has it been understood how constantly present the influences of space are around and within us. A few years ago, no one had any idea why chemical or biological reactions could vary from day to day despite all precautions to the contrary. The fact is, as far as liquids are concerned, there are never any constant conditions. Of course identical laboratory experiments with solids would not give similar results, since the organization of solid systems is almost unmodifiable; weak·influences have no effect on it. But solids are not life.

Life is the unstable equilibrium of the liquid element. No amount of precaution can shield the unstable structure of liquids from the effects of outside forces. It is not chance but a permanent law of nature that makes experiments with liquids difficult to reproduce from one hour to the next. According to Piccardi's apt formulation, these are "fluctuating phenomena." Is this a reason for giving up the idea of studying them? It should not be.* On the contrary, it is necessary to take into account the *exact moment* at which the reaction occurs; this is almost as important a factor as the chemical means by which the experiment is conducted, because at any given instant the cosmos may act, leaving in its wake an imprint that may change the conditions of the experiment. The young lab assistant we mentioned at the beginning of this chapter had no doubt taken all the possible precautions for the success of his experiment, but he overlooked the hourly

---

*A few years ago, a University Center for the Study of Fluctuating Phenomena was created in Florence; under the leadership of G. Piccardi, it has attained a worldwide reputation.

influence of the cosmos on the unfolding of earthly events. This is why chemical reactions succeed one day and fail the next; this is why physiological accidents fall on man like a thunderbolt from the sky; this is how the strange behavior of birth mechanisms with respect to the planetary clocks can be explained.

As Cloudsley-Thompson, the zoologist, has asked: Is the organism itself a clock, or does it contain a clock? In these pages there has emerged an explanatory theory to answer this question. It does not seem that living beings have a specific sense organ that allows them to perceive separately each of the newly discovered influences. Probably it is the body in its entirety that constantly reacts to environmental rhythms. The body as a whole may be both a biological clock and a biological compass; very likely it can also "perceive" even finer nuances, such as those emanating from the closest planets. All this can happen through the mediation of the alterable structures of the organism: the water and the colloids of which it is mostly made. It is therefore probable that, as Piccardi said,

> The action of extraterrestrial forces does not concern any given organ, any given illness, any given biological function, but the complex state of living matter. Organisms have to maintain their vital conditions as far as possible, and to do this they have to react to the fluctuating properties of their environment, to fight in order to keep them stable. This results in a deep-set 'fatigue' of all the colloidal systems of the organism, of all its material substance. It could be said that it is the living matter as a whole that is so disturbed.[23]

Without the ability to react readily to external influences, life would be impossible. The external dialogue between man and space seems to be indispensable to our survival.

NOTES TO CHAPTER TWELVE

1. G. Piccardi, "Exposé introductif," *Symposium Intern. sur les Rel. Phén. Sol. et Terr.* (Brussells: Presses Académiques Européennes, 1960).
2. H. Bortels, "Beziehungen zwischen Witterungsablauf, physikalisch-chemischen Reaktionen, biologischem Geschehen und Sonnenaktivität," *Naturwissenschaften,* XXXVIII (1951), 165.
3. E. Findeisen, "Experimentelle Untersuchungen über den Einfluss des Witterungsablaufes auf die Beständigkeit eines Kolloids," *Bioklimat. Beibl.,* X (1943), 23.
4. J. Cloudsley-Thompson, *Rhythmic Activity in Animal Physiology and Behaviour* (New York: Academic Press, 1961).
5. Piccardi, *op. cit.*
6. *Ibid.*
7. *Ibid.*
8. C. Capel-Boute, "Observations sur les tests chimiques de Piccardi," *Symp. Intern. sur les Phén. Sol. et Terr.* (Brussells: Presses Académiques Européennes, 1960).
9. D. Barber, "Apparent Solar Control of the Effective Capacity of a 110-V. 170 AH Lead-Acid Storage Battery in an Eleven-Year Cycle," *Nature,* CXCV (1962), 684.
10. G. Papeschi and M. Costa, "First Results on the Relations Between the Naphthalene Test and the Lunar Phases," *Geofis. e Meteorol.,* XIV (1965), No. 3-4, 79.
11. A. Rima, "Sui possibili Rapporti fra le fasi lunari e l'andamento dei test chimici Piccardi," *Geofis. e Meteorol.,* VIII (1964), No. 1-2, 3.
12. C. Duval, *L'eau* (Paris: P.U.F., 1962), p. 6.
13. J. Bernal and R. Fowler, "A Theory of Water and Ionic Solution with Particular Reference to Hydrogene and Hydroxyl Ions," *Journal of Chemical Physics,* I (1953), 515.
14. H.S. Frank, "The Structure of Water," *Federation Proceedings,* XXIV (1965), 2.
15. J. Pople, "A Theory of the Structure of Water," *Proceedings of the Royal Society,* A, CCII (1950), 323.

16. S. Bordi and F. Vannel, "Variazione giornaliera di grandezze chimicofisiche. Conducibilità elettrica," *Geofis. e Meteorol.,* XIV (1965), 28.

17. W. Fisher, G. Sturdy, M. Ryan, and R. Pugh, "Some Laboratory Studies of Fluctuating Phenomena," Fourth International Biometeorological Congress (in preparation).

18. M. Magat, "Change of Properties of Water around 40° C.," *Journal Phys. Radium,* VI (1936), 108.

19. G. Piccardi, *The Chemical Basis of Medical Climatology* (Springfield, Ill.: Charles Thomas, 1962).

20. *Ibid.*

21. G. Piccardi, "Exposé introductif," *op. cit.*

22. F. A. Brown, Jr., "Extrinsic Timing of Rhythms," *Annals of the New York Academy of Science,* XCVIII (1962), 775.

23. G. Piccardi, "Exposé introductif," *op. cit.*

From Light-Gods
to Planetary Clocks

An ANCIENT hermetic text, the *Emerald Table,* states,

> It is truth, not a lie, it's true and very certain: That which is up high is like that which is below and that which is below is like that which is up high.

These lines express the first intuitions of our ancestors about the relationship of man to the universe surrounding him. They describe in enigmatic terms the esoteric doctrine according to which man is a universe in miniature, built on the model of the cosmic universe. Man is a microcosm, it used to be said, the heavens are the macrocosm, and between the two run close currents of sympathy.

Modern science has not retained the occult aspect of this venerable lesson. The sky is not a magic mirror in which our pleasures and pains are reflected. But science does teach us that the whole universe is reflected in a drop of water, that the cosmic rhythms are necessary to the survival of life. Thus we begin to see that our bodies are in fact tied with invisible strings to the cosmos, as was dimly realized in the past. But these strings are not held by planetary gods who make us perform like puppets; they are fields of force known as electricity, magnetism, and gravitation.

In the alchemy books of the Middle Ages there is an idea for those searching for the Philosopher's Stone. This idea, which has survived through the generations, is that certain celestial configurations "seal" the magical reaction the alchemist is attempting to perform in his alembics. The alchemists were also astrologers, and their hoary parchments tell in great detail how, in order to change lead into gold, the favorable celestial configuration that alone will allow the transformation to take place has to be selected. Science today has given up the quest for the Philosopher's Stone; yet it now teaches us that a specific cosmic "seal" does affect various physical, chemical, and biological reactions.

Another ancient teaching says that apparently insignificant changes can, with time, transform chemical compounds. This is why the alchemist had to mix his ingredients constantly, day after day, until the base metal would progressively change itself into shining gold. Modern physics achieves the transmutation of elements with the aid of huge cyclotrons, in which matter is bombarded with electrons, developing very high energy states. But scientists have also discovered the importance of the very low energies that modify the structure of water. And liquids are the structural basis of life, which has all the fragility of its component elements.

In the fourth century B.C., Hippocrates stated: "The space between the earth and the sky is filled with spirit. The very movements of the sun, the moon, and the stars are caused by the blowing of this spirit." The Chaldeans also believed in a "living" ether. Artificial satellites orbiting around the globe have failed to find gods in the sky, but their instruments have shown that what was thought thirty years ago to be the "interstellar void" is in reality filled with matter and with energy. The magnetospheric wakes of the planets dance a perpetual ballet in the fields of force of the sun and the galaxy.

We must acknowledge the merits of those men who, in the past, with the inadequate means at their disposal, tried to understand the nature and the influence of the stars. A clay tablet covered with cuneiform script reads: "A halo surrounding the moon-god is a sign of rain." Our meteorologists are discovering that extensive rains can be influenced by lunar movements. The pharaohs deified the sun and attributed to it a thousand magic powers. We know now that the sun has been acting on life since its beginnings, by contributing to its creation, preservation, and, sometimes, its destruction. The theory of "astral signatures" so dear to ancient astrology reappears in the effect of the planetary clocks on birth. It gives one pause to consider the possibility of scientifically establishing a prediction based on the hour of a man's birth. A link has already been found between planetary rhythms and some types of human activity. The statistically significant relationship between Mars and doctors, athletes, and military men may foreshadow a spectacular comeback of the old Chaldean symbolism into our intellectual life.

It would be presumptuous to insist that man never gained a glimpse of the truth in six thousand years of astrological investigations. The alchemist Brandt discovered phosphorus by chance in 1669 while searching for the Philosopher's Stone. Yet we should not confuse chemistry with alchemy or biometeorology with astrology. We have seen that glimmers of truth have been prematurely interpreted and distorted and that the early correct intuitions about the cosmic influences on man have degenerated into myth and superstition.

Science today reveals and explains cosmic influences to us in new terms, divorced from magic and astrology. In place of magic, new scientific disciplines based on research are being developed. They are still only partly recognized because of their recent origins. Dr. S. Tromp of the University of Leyden, in addressing the World Academy of Arts and Sciences, called them the border sciences, adding: "They comprise those types of fundamental research which penetrate into completely unknown realms of human knowledge, until recently considered the domain of vague, unrealistic quasi-scientists and unfortunately often the hunting-ground of unscientific charlatans."

Two border sciences are working in the field reclaimed from astrology: the first is biometeorology, which studies the influence of atmospheric and cosmic conditions on life; the second is the study of the meaning and relevance of biological rhythms. Two international scientific societies represent the two disciplines: the International Society of Biometeorology (ISB) and the Society for Biological Rhythms (SBR).

As for the intriguing hereditary effects that have been discovered in the study of planetary rhythms, no occult meaning is to be read into them. In fact, they support a concept that is the opposite of astrological predestination. The moon and the planets are not the miraculous determinants of our future. The sky of birth does not add anything a child lacks within himself. The effect of the stars does not change the character of the newborn, does not set the future in a happy or an unhappy direction. The willful power of the star-gods has been supplanted by the indifferent, if real, action of the planetary clocks.

But this should not prevent us from being grateful for the bumbling beliefs of the astrologers. If we had not been challenged to check their fantastic claims, we wouldn't have discovered the existence of planetary clocks. We see now that the idea that man can be affected by the surrounding sky is a normal one. When men of the past ages intuited this world of astral influences, they approached it with the structures of primitive thought; around it they built up myths, at times ingenious and profound, that still inhabit the depths of our collective unconscious, as Jung has shown.

But it is time for a rigorous investigation of these phenomena to take the place of the dreamy search for the key to the stars. Of course, man's unconscious is slow to change. His fear of the future makes him prefer an occult, superstitious explanation to scientific explanations based on reason. We have seen that astrology as an intellectual discipline has been stagnant almost from its beginnings. Nowadays, in the hands of ignorant fortune tellers, it has become the caricature of a science for the use of the weak and the idle. Respectable cosmic thought, detached from its sources, has sunk to the level of a gossipy confidence game. But it is possible to retrace the steps to the source.

As he walked up the seven stories of his observation tower, the Chaldean priest believed that he was climbing almost within reach of heaven. His hope seems foolish today, yet moving and understandable. His eyes and his thoughts focused on the messages from his gods; far above the dust of the cities, the priest conversed with the universe as with an equal. There is an astonishing continuity between his attitude and the one that today prompts mankind to expend treasures of courage and ingeniousness to leave the earth for the beckoning stars. The astronaut inside his capsule who lets out an admiring shout at the beauty of the surrounding sky he sees for the first time from such a height can think with thanks of his predecessors, the astrologer priests. He can remember without contempt the proud confession of Ptolemy, the "prince of astrologers":

"Mortal as I am, I know that I am born for a day, but when I follow the serried multitude of the stars in their circular course, my feet no longer touch the earth; I ascend to Zeus himself to feast me on ambrosia, the food of the gods."

APPENDIX I

METHODOLOGY AND STATISTICAL ANALYSIS

The following brief summary will relate the main scientific principles underlying the conclusions presented in Chapter Eleven on planetary influences on successful vocations.

The Diurnal Movement

Each day, as a result of the earth's rotation on itself, the sun, the moon, the planets, and the stars describe around the earth a twenty-four-hour trajectory called the diurnal movement.

Let us consider, for instance, the diurnal movement of Mars on May 24, 1956, in Paris. In the *Yearbook of the Bureau of Longitudes* we find that on that day, in Paris, Mars rose at 0 hours 44 minutes, culminated at 5 h. 33 m., and set at 10 h. 22 m., to rise again the next morning about the same time as on the previous day.

In Figure 13, two perpendicular circles indicate the horizon and the meridian of the locality. The diurnal movement of Mars occurs around the circle ABCDA. In our example, when the trajectory of Mars cuts across the eastern horizon, the planet is rising; it is 0 h. 44 m. (point A). Then it climbs across the sky until it reaches the highest point of its ascent, culminating at the meridian; it is 5 h. 33 m. (point B). The planet descends toward the western horizon, where it disappears at 10 h. 22 m. (point C). Underneath the earth, it follows a path that completes the trajectory it went through above the horizon. It reaches the lower point of its course when it again crosses the meridian (point D). From then on it comes up again toward the horizon, over which it will again appear close to point A.

It is obvious that the position of the planet as seen from the earth changes at a uniform rate, from hour to hour. In our example if a person had been born on May 24, 1956, at one o'clock in the morning, we would say that Mars was then rising. If the birth had occurred at six o'clock, it would be said that the planet had just culminated and begun its descent toward the horizon. At any time of the day or night all the planets of the solar system

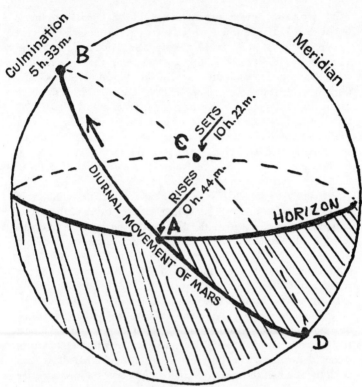

Fig. 13—*Diurnal movement of Mars on May 26, 1956, in Paris.*

are placed at different points between the horizon and the meridian; their positions can be traced down quite easily with the help of information contained in astronomical yearbooks.

The Division of the Diurnal Movement into Sectors

The research samples mentioned in Chapter Eleven include thousands of birth dates, which fall into thousands of possible positions along the diurnal movement of each planet. In order to perform a statistical analysis on the frequency of births at each position, it becomes necessary to divide the diurnal movement into sectors. This enables us to group together births that occurred while the planet was in the same region of the sky.

But according to what procedure should the diurnal movement be divided? Let us continue with the example presented in Figure 13 and developed in Figure 14. On May 24, 1956, Mars rose at 0 h. 44 m. and set at 10 h. 22 m., thereby remaining above the horizon for 9 hours and 38 minutes, or 578 minutes altogether. Consequently, on that day the planet remained invisible below the horizon for 862 minutes. For that day, the diurnal arc of Mars is 578 minutes, and its nocturnal arc is 862 minutes. Suppose that we want to divide the diurnal movement into twelve sectors. Mars will remain in each of its diurnal sectors for the same length of time; in this case: 578/6 = 96 minutes in each sector. It will remain in each of the nocturnal sectors 862/6 = 144 minutes.

It is easier to see what we are talking about if we number the twelve sectors from 1 to 12, beginning with the rising of the planet and proceeding clockwise in the direction of the diurnal movement (see Fig. 14). On May 24, 1956, Mars remained in sector one from 0 h. 44 m. to 2 h. 20 m., in sector two from 2 h. 20 m. to 3 h. 57 m. The figure shows the times at which the planet passes from one sector to the next.

If a person is born at one o'clock in the morning of that day, we would then not only say that he was born when Mars was rising, but, more accurately, that he was born when Mars was in sector one. If the birth occurred at six o'clock, we would say that Mars was in sector four, instead of saying that it had just culminated. At each birth the sun and the other celestial bodies occupy a specific sector of their diurnal movement, and it is easy to record the numbers of the sectors in which they were at a given date. In a sample of several thousand births, there will be a few hundred at which Mars was in sector 1, a few hundred in sector 2, and so on. The same applies to all other planets. The observed frequencies of births during the diurnal movements of the planets were distributed into such abstract "sectors."

The Computation of Theoretical Frequencies

After one has observed how often a given planet appears in each sector for a specific sample of births, the question becomes whether there is a real relationship between the position of the planet and the frequency of births. In order to answer the question, it is necessary to compare the actually *observed* distribution with the dis-

CULMINATION

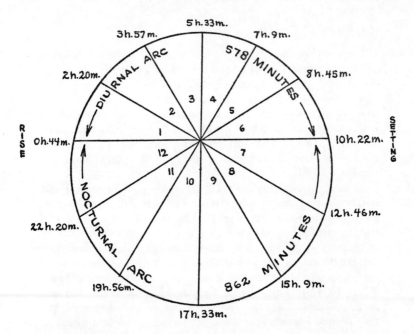

Fig. 14—*Division of the diurnal movement of Mars into twelve sectors.*

tribution *expected* if the same number of births had been chosen at random. The problem is that even in a sample of births taken perfectly at random, a planet will not be found an equal number of times in each sector.

So the theoretical, expected frequency depends on two different orders of phenomena: the first, purely astronomical one, depends on the relative lengths of the diurnal and nocturnal arcs of the planet in question; the second is a function of the irregular rhythm of births throughout the day.

Here we will limit ourselves to show succinctly the role that each of these phenomena plays, since the problem is examined in detail, with several numerical examples, in our work *Méthodes pour Étudier la Répartition des Astres dans le Mouvement Diurne*

(Paris, 1957). The first order of phenomena will be called "astronomical conditions," the second "demographic conditions."*

Astronomical Conditions

The shape of the frequency distribution of a planet's position at birth depends, first of all, on the planet's astronomical conditions during the time-span in question.

If we return to our illustration, it will be clear that while the time the planet spends in each diurnal sector will be the same, it will differ from the time it spends in each nocturnal sector. Thus on May 24, 1956, in the northern hemisphere, more children were born with Mars in nocturnal sectors than in diurnal ones (*see* Fig. 14).

As time passes, the respective lengths of a planet's diurnal and nocturnal arcs change progressively.† The probability for the presence of a planet in a diurnal sector changes systematically as a ratio with the probability of its presence in a nocturnal sector. It is easy to understand the statistical consequences of such a difference if we take the sun as an example. Suppose that in a sample there are many more June births than December ones. Since in our hemisphere days are much longer in June than in December, our sample will have many more persons who were born during the day than persons who were born at night. In such a sample it would be more probable for the sun to be in a diurnal sector than in a nocturnal sector. The same argument holds, of course, for the other bodies in the solar system.

It is therefore necessary to compute the average time that each planet spent in the diurnal and nocturnal segments of its arc, for the total birth dates of each sample. This will enable us to calcu-

---

* These two phenomena are not related to all the bodies of the solar system equally. In our research, neither of them applied to Jupiter or to the moon. The positions of Saturn, Uranus, Neptune, and Pluto were affected by astronomical conditions; those of Mars by both; while those of the sun, Mercury, and Venus were mostly sensitive to demographic conditions.

† As a function of the planet's apparent circling of the earth on the ecliptic (due to the fact that both the earth and the planet are rotating around the sun), the declination of the planet changes, with the effect that day by day the trajectory of the planet as seen from the earth seems to change. When the declination is positive, the diurnal arc is longer than the nocturnal one; when the declination becomes negative the opposite relationship holds.

late the theoretically expected astronomical frequencies for the planet in each of the six diurnal and the six nocturnal sectors. (*See* Part III of *Méthodes.*)

Demographic Conditions

In Chapter Ten, some of the works that proved how the frequency of births through the twenty-four hours of the day varies were quoted. It is not necessary here to present in detail all the irregularities that were found; it is enough to state the general rule that natural childbirths occur much more frequently in the morning than in the afternoon hours.

The irregular pattern of births through the day affects the probability of the presence of certain planets in the sectors of their diurnal movement—those planets whose apparent movements are tied to the apparent movement of the sun. In fact, the theoretical frequency of the sun's presence would be far from regular in any sample of birthdates. There is a higher probability for the sun to appear in the sectors corresponding to the peak of births, and the inverse also holds true. For instance, more than an average number of children are born at six in the morning, when the sun rises; thus theoretically one would expect more than an average number of children to be born with the sun in sector one.

The consequences of this demographic phenomenon are especially relevant to Mercury, Venus, and Mars, since these planets are often seen from earth as being in the same regions as the sun. The probability of their presence in a sector is affected by the irregular rhythm of births through the day, although less so than in the case of the sun itself.

For each given sample of births, it is therefore necessary to compute also the theoretically expected demographic frequency of the position of each planet in every sector of its diurnal movement. These are not easy calculations; one has to take into account both the distances of the planet from the sun and the general distribution of births observed during the various hours of the day. Numerical examples are given in *Méthodes.*

Statistics

After computing for each given planet and sample the theoretically expected frequency for each sector, corrected for astronomical and demographic conditions, it then becomes possible to calculate whether there is a statistically significant difference between the expected and the observed frequencies. The essential question is whether the difference is or is not too large to attribute to the effect of chance. The law of probabilities enables us to compute the level at which the difference between the expected and observed frequencies becomes too large for it to be caused by chance. The method most appropriate in this case is the computation of the standard score, as expressed by the formula:

$$\frac{x - m}{\sqrt{npq}} = \text{standard score}$$

where x = the observed number, m = the expected number, and $\sqrt{npq}$ = the standard deviation of the variable x.

After the formula is calculated, the result is checked in the appropriate table (a table of normal distribution) to find out what probability level should be given to the normal score found. The appropriate level will tell how significantly above chance were the observed differences in the presence of planets at birth in the sectors of rising and culmination.

In statistical practice, an experimental finding is called "significant" when the probability that chance could have caused the results goes below a certain level of likelihood. Statisticians attribute a "low level of significance" to results that could be caused by chance once out of ten (or .1 level; standard score 1.64); a "significant" result is one with a chance probability of one in twenty (or .05 level; standard score 1.96); a "highly significant" result is one with a chance probability of one in a hundred (or .01 level; standard score 2.58).

APPENDIX II

PICCARDI'S CHEMICAL TESTS

In order to gain as complete knowledge as possible about the effects of space, Piccardi decided to vary three factors at the same time. First, to check whether external influences affected chemical reactions, one had to shield the test tubes by means of a screen. Then, in order to determine whether the conditions inside the test tube were the crucial ones, it was necessary to have two different test conditions; specifically, a test tube containing normal water, and another one filled with activated water.

With such an experimental design, Piccardi had three routine tests done every day for several years. The observations consisted of recording the speed with which the inorganic colloid bismuth oxychloride precipitated. This colloid, which is normally insoluble in water, is prepared by pouring bismuth trichloride into water. As a result the colloid precipitates, but *at a variable speed.* It is this variability that interested Piccardi.

Test F: There are two test tubes, one containing normal water, the other activated water. The two containers are unshielded. The speed with which the bismuth oxychloride precipitates in normal water is compared with that in activated water. The question is, how will cosmic phenomena affect the two reaction times?

Test D: The same two containers, but this time they are shielded. The question is whether the shield will cut off or modify cosmic influences differentially for the normal and the activated water. The criterion is again the comparison between the precipitation speeds of the bismuth oxychloride.

Test P: The two test tubes are both filled with normal water, but one is kept outdoors while the other is shielded by a screen. The question is whether the screen will modify the speed of precipitation, which ought to be the same as that of the test tube left outdoors if the influences of space have no effect on reaction.

TABLES

TABLE I
Selected Characteristics of the Planets

	Mercury	Venus	Earth	Moon (in relation to the earth)	Mars	Jupiter	Saturn	Uranus	Neptune	Plato
Average distance from the sun	0.39	0.72	1.00	—	1.52	5.20	9.55	19.21	30.11	39.52
Sidereal revolution	88 days	224.7 days	1 year	27 days 32	1 year 322	11 years 315	29 years 167	84 years 7	164 years 280	248 years 157
Synodic revolution	115.9 days	1 year 218	—	29 days 53	2 years 50	1 year 34	1 year 12	1 year 4	1 year 2	1 year 1
Mass (Earth = 1)	0.045	0.81	1.00	$\frac{1}{81.5}$	0.11	317	95	14.7	17.2	0.8
Density (Water = 1)	4.1	4.9	5.52	3.33	3.9	1.34	0.71	1.27	1.6	5.5(?)
Rotation over itself	88 days	225 days(?)	23 h. 56 m. 45 s.	27 days 3	24 h. 37 m. 23 s.	9 h. 50 m.	10 h. 14 m.	10 h. 42 m.	15 h. 48 m.	?
Apparent diameter	5" to 13"	10" to 64"	—	31'	3" to 25"	31" to 50"	15" to 21"	3" to 4"	2"	0.2"(?)

TABLE II

Solar and Geomagnetic Activity from 1900 to 1939

Year	R	Ci	Year	R	Ci
1900	9.5	0.42	1920	37.6	0.62
1901	2.7	0.45	1921	26.1	0.61
1902	5.0	0.44	1922	14.2	0.64
1903	24.4	0.59	1923	5.8	0.48
1904	42.0	0.55	1924	16.7	0.54
1905	*63.5*	0.59	1925	44.3	0.56
1906	53.8	0.65	1926	63.9	0.65
1907	62.0	0.66	1927	69.0	0.63
1908	48.5	0.68	1928	*77.8*	0.63
1909	43.9	0.62	1929	64.9	0.67
1910	18.6	0.72	1930	35.7	0.83
1911	5.7	0.63	1931	21.2	0.66
1912	3.6	0.46	1932	11.1	0.70
1913	1.4	0.48	1933	5.7	0.64
1914	9.6	0.54	1934	8.7	0.56
1915	47.4	0.62	1935	36.1	0.57
1916	57.1	0.71	1936	79.7	0.65
1917	*103.9*	0.66	1937	*114.4*	0.74
1918	80.6	0.75	1938	109.6	0.74
1919	63.6	0.72	1939	88.8	0.76

Solar activity is measured by the relative number of sunspots (Wolf's number, according to the formula $R = K[10. g + f]$). Peak years are set italic. They occur, on the average, every eleven years. Geomagnetic activity is measured by the International Magnetic Character Figure (Ci). Ci varies from 0.0 (quiet days) to 2.0 (days of intense magnetic storms). It is measured daily at specialized observatories throughout the world. The annual values of Ci co-vary with the relative number of sunspots (R).

References: M. Waldmeier, *The Sunspot Activity in the years 1610-1960* (Zurich: Schulthess & Co., 1961), p. 21; J. Bartels, A. Romana, and J. Veldkamp, *IAGA Bulletin, Geomagnetic Data No. 12, p. 1* (UNESCO, 1964), p. 94.

TABLE III

The Planets and Vocations

Professions that show an unusual frequency (plus or minus) in the number of births after the rise or culmination of the planets.[1]

Planet	Profession	Number of births	Observed frequency of births at rise or culmination of planet	Expected frequency of births at rise or culmination of planet	Difference	Probability that difference is due to chance
Mars						
	Scientists and Physicians	3,305	666	566	+100	1 in 500,000
	Athletes	1,485	327	253	+74	1 in 5,000,000
	Military Men	3,142	634	536	+98	1 in 1,000,000
	Painters	1,345	188	229	−41	1 in 300
	Musicians	703	94	120	−26	1 in 100
	Writers	826	117	142	−25	1 in 40

TABLE III (Continued)

Planet	Profession	Number of births	Observed frequency of births at rise or culmination of planet	Expected frequency of births at rise or culmination of planet	Difference	Probability that difference is due to chance
Jupiter	Military Men	3,142	644	526	+98	1 in 5,000,000
	Politicians	993	208	164	+44	1 in 5,000
	Actors	1,270	252	211	+41	1 in 500
	Journalists	824	168	137	+31	1 in 200
	Scientists and Physicians	3,305	497	546	−49	1 in 50
Saturn	Scientists and Physicians	3,305	632	540	+92	1 in 100,000
	Painters	1,345	178	217	−39	1 in 250
	Writers	826	108	136	−28	1 in 130
Moon	Politicians	858	173	143	+30	1 in 200
	Writers	826	180	138	+42	1 in 15,000
	Athletes	1,485	211	248	−37	1 in 200

1 The astronomical definition of the rising and culminating sectors is given in Appendix I. (Data from Gauquelin, *Les Hommes et les Astres* [Paris: Denöel, 1960].)

TABLE IV

Effects of Solar Eruptions on Piccardi's "F" Test

Year	Days before −4	−3	−2	−1	Day of eruption 0	Days after +1	+2	+3	+4
1951	54	58	60	60	64	60	56	56	55
1952	45	44	40	41	55	39	41	46	47
1953	44	40	42	46	57	40	49	44	45

The numbers are the average values of the chemical reactions added together year by year. The effect of solar eruptions is highly evident for the individual years.

(After G. Piccardi, *The Chemical Basis of Medical Climatology*, p. 87.)

Index

1 2 3 4 5 6 7 ← P Y → 9 8 7 6 5 4